GRADE 3

Reader's and Writer's Journal TEACHER'S GUIDE

PEARSON

Glenview, Illinois • Boston, Massachusetts • Chandler, Arizona • Hoboken, New Jersey

PEARSON

ISBN-13: 978-0-328-85165-2
ISBN-10: 0-328-85165-5
5 16

Table of Contents

Unit 1 Observing the World Around Us

Unit 2 Connecting Character, Culture, and Community

Unit 3 Seeking Explanations

Module A

Module B

Unit 4 Becoming an Active Citizen

Module A

Module B

Name ______________________________

Short Vowels and Syllables VC/CV

DIRECTIONS Choose the word with the **short vowel** sound in the **first syllable** to complete each sentence. Write the word on the line.

1. My mom works in a big (hotel/hospital). hospital
2. She got the job last (April/winter). winter
3. She is a (doctor/writer). doctor
4. Mom also writes (papers/letters). letters
5. She does most of her writing on a (tablet/tabletop). tablet

DIRECTIONS Circle the word with the **short vowel** sound in the **first syllable**. Then underline the letter that stands for that short vowel sound.

6. happen	higher	hoses
7. miner	problem	music
8. painter	private	puppet
9. lately	lettuce	likely
10. trial	toaster	ticket
11. napkin	native	notebook
12. spoken	spider	spotlight
13. baby	blender	bleacher
14. sister	safety	season
15. guidebook	gutter	grateful

Students apply grade-level phonics and word analysis skills.

Benchmark Vocabulary

Name ______________________________

DIRECTIONS Write a sentence using each word.

location overtime

Responses should show contextual understanding of the word.

Write in Response to Reading

Read p. 26 from the *Text Collection*. Write several sentences that describe Evan's actions, motivations, and feelings.

Responses may vary but should include that Evan was in a contest with his sister and he wanted to beat her, and he was worried because he was behind.

Students demonstrate contextual understanding of Benchmark Vocabulary. Students read text closely and use text evidence in their written answers.

Name ______________________________

Tell a Story Write a paragraph describing a story you would like to tell.

Responses will vary but should include a description of a story the student would like to tell.

Nouns

DIRECTIONS Write the nouns in the sentences.

1. Evan dragged his wagon to the center of the town.

Evan, wagon, center, town

2. Evan went to the desk and worked on some problems.

Evan, desk, problems

3. It was lunchtime and the shaded benches were filled with people.

lunchtime, benches, people

Students write routinely for a range of tasks, purposes, and audiences. Students practice various conventions of standard English.

Benchmark Vocabulary

Name ______________________________

DIRECTIONS Write a sentence using the word.

competition

Responses should show contextual understanding of the word.

Write in Response to Reading

Read the last two paragraphs on p. 32 from the *Text Collection*. Write a paragraph that explains the sequence of events in the two paragraphs that you read. Include words and phrases that show the order of events.

Sample response: First Evan wheeled his wagon off to the side and parked it. After that he crossed the street and walked into the Big Dipper. He then looked at the ice cream, and the money in his pocket tingled. He wondered about spending some of his money.

Students demonstrate contextual understanding of Benchmark Vocabulary. Students read text closely and use text evidence in their written answers.

Name ______________________________

Temporal Words and Phrases

DIRECTIONS Using evidence from the text, answer the following questions about "Location, Location, Location."

1. Read the second paragraph on p. 32 of "Location, Location, Location." What temporal words and phrases does the author use?

first, then

2. Explain how these words show the sequence of events.

Responses will vary but should include that "first" tells the reader what happened first and "then" tells the reader what happened next.

3. Read the last two paragraphs on p. 34 of "Location, Location, Location." What temporal words and phrases does the author use?

first, then, when, for a full hour

4. What other words could the author have used to show the order of events?

Responses will vary but could include "after that" and "next."

Students analyze and respond to literary and informational text.

Name ______________________________

Writing

Describe a Setting Look back at the character and problem you wrote about in Lesson 1, and decide whether they are realistic or not. Decide on an appropriate setting for your story, and write a paragraph describing it.

Responses will vary but should include an appropriate setting for the student's character and problem.

Conventions

Nouns as Subjects of Sentences

DIRECTIONS Write the subject of the following sentences:

1. But today was Friday. **today**

2. His brain spun like a top. **brain**

3. The Jacksons went to Florida last summer. **The Jacksons**

Students write routinely for a range of tasks, purposes, and audiences. Students practice various conventions of standard English.

Benchmark Vocabulary

Name ______________________________

DIRECTIONS Write a sentence using each word.

location competition

Responses should show contextual understanding of the word.

Write in Response to Reading

Read pp. 38–39 from the *Text Collection*. What is your opinion of Evan's solution to his problem? State your opinion and support it using evidence from the text.

Responses should use evidence from the text.

Students demonstrate contextual understanding of Benchmark Vocabulary. Students read text closely and use text evidence in their written answers.

Name ______________________________

Getting Organized

Mrs. Rodriguez asked her students to turn in their homework. Cora's stomach sank because she didn't have her homework. She remembered to do it, but she forgot to put it in her backpack. It was still sitting on the kitchen table.

"Cora," Mrs. Rodriguez said, "did you forget to do your homework again?"

"No," Cora looked down at her feet. "I did the homework, but I left it at home."

"I'm sorry to hear that, Cora," Mrs. Rodriguez said. "Bring it in tomorrow, but you will lose five points."

That night the phone rang. "Hello, Mrs. Rodriguez," Cora heard her mother answer. *This cannot be good*, Cora thought.

"Of course, I will talk to Cora."

"Cora," Mama said, "Mrs. Rodriguez says your missing and late assignments are going to affect your grade. That's a problem."

"I'm sorry," Cora said. "I'm always in such a rush in the morning. It's hard to remember everything."

"Cora, rather than being sorry," Mama said, "I want you to solve this problem. You're too smart to let a lack of organization get in the way of good grades."

"What can I do, Mama?" Cora asked.

"Let's think of some ways you can be more organized," Mama said.

Cora came up with three solutions to her problem:

1. Write down my assignments.
2. Get ready for school the night before.
3. Have Mama double-check my homework.

Three weeks later, Cora brought home her report card. Mama gave her a hug. Cora's solutions had worked!

Students read text closely to determine what the text says.

Name ______________________________

Gather Evidence Underline 3–4 details about Cora's problem in the text on p. 8. In another color, box the 2 that are most important. Write them below. See annotations on previous page.

Boxed responses may vary but could include that Cora is always in such a rush in the morning and Cora forgot to put her homework in her backpack.

Gather Evidence: Extend Your Ideas Work with a partner, and discuss how changing just one of these details would affect the story.

Responses will vary.

Ask Questions Write two questions that the teacher might have asked Cora about why Cora's homework wasn't turned in on time. Bracket the words in the text that could answer the questions.

Sample response: Where is your homework? Student would bracket "It was still sitting on the kitchen table."

Ask Questions: Extend Your Ideas Write an additional question that the teacher could have asked Cora that is answered in the text. Circle the answer in the text.

Responses should use evidence from the text.

Make Your Case Draw an arrow from Cora's decision (a cause) about changing her habits to what happens (the effect) at the end of the story.

See annotation on previous page.

Make Your Case: Extend Your Ideas Identify other causes that lead to other effects. Discuss your results with a partner.

Responses will vary.

Students read text closely to determine what the text says.

Writing

Name ______________________________

Provide Closure Write a one-paragraph narrative based on the character, problem, and setting you wrote about in Lessons 1 and 2. First, introduce your character, your setting, and the problem the character must solve. Then, add events and a solution to the problem that provides a satisfying ending to the story.

Responses will vary but should include a narrative paragraph that includes a character, a setting, and a problem the character must solve.

Conventions

Form and Use Regular Plural Nouns

DIRECTIONS Create a sentence using the plural form of each noun.

1. kid **The kids went outside to play.**

2. finger **Her fingers were cold.**

3. watch **I have purchased five watches this year.**

Students write routinely for a range of tasks, purposes, and audiences. Students practice various conventions of standard English.

Benchmark Vocabulary

Name ________________________________

DIRECTIONS Write a sentence using each word.

solution overwhelm efficient

Responses should show contextual understanding of the word.

Write in Response to Reading

Read pp. 2–3 of *The Case of the Gasping Garbage*. Write a short narrative from Gabby's point of view that tells what happens before she calls Drake and asks for his help. Use evidence from the text to establish the details and events.

Responses should use evidence from the text, including that Gabby was home alone and heard noises coming from her garbage can. She was afraid it was a monster that would eat her.

Students demonstrate contextual understanding of Benchmark Vocabulary. Students read text closely and use text evidence in their written answers.

Writing

Name ______________________________

Introduce a Character and Setting Write a narrative paragraph that introduces a character and an interesting setting. First, introduce one character by telling the most important details the reader should know about him or her. Then introduce a setting for the character by describing the place and time clearly.

Responses will vary but should include a narrative paragraph that introduces a character and a setting.

Conventions

Identify Verbs

DIRECTIONS Read p. 3 of *The Case of the Gasping Garbage*. Find five words that are verbs, and write them on the line below.

Responses will vary but could include the following verbs: pushed, set, shrieked, talk, speak, gasped, publish, lecture.

Students write routinely for a range of tasks, purposes, and audiences. Students practice various conventions of standard English.

Benchmark Vocabulary

Name ______________________________

DIRECTIONS Write a sentence using each word.

affirmative   observations   hypothesis   mediums   culprit

Responses should show contextual understanding of the word.

Write in Response to Reading

Read pp. 13–15 of *The Case of the Gasping Garbage*. Using evidence from the text, write an explanation of the procedure (steps) that Drake and Nell use to solve the garbage can problem.

Responses will vary but should include that Drake and Nell performed experiments on the trash can, including tapping on the can, lifting it to see how heavy it was, copying the warm environment where the can was stored, and noticing that the can smelled like bread.

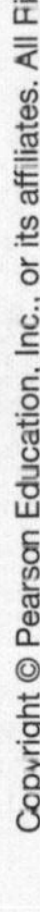

Students demonstrate contextual understanding of Benchmark Vocabulary. Students read text closely and use text evidence in their written answers.

Name ______________________

Reading Analysis

Parts of Stories

DIRECTIONS Using evidence from the text, answer the following questions about Chapters 1 and 2 from *The Case of the Gasping Garbage*.

1. Who are the characters in Chapter 1? Who are the characters in Chapter 2?

   Drake Doyle, Nell Fossey, Gabby Talberg, James Frisco; Drake Doyle, Nell Fossey, Kate Doyle, Sam Doyle, Professor Fossey, Gabby Talberg

2. Why are some characters the same in the two chapters? Why are some characters different?

   Responses should include evidence from the text.

3. What settings are the same in both chapters?

   Drake Doyle's lab/house

4. What are the most important events in Chapter 1? Why are they important?

   Drake and Nell get a case to solve. They are science detectives who solve cases.

5. What are the most important events in Chapter 2? Why are they important?

   Drake and Nell solve their case. They are science detectives, and people depend on them to solve their problems.

Students analyze and respond to literary and informational text.

Writing

Name ____________________

Write a Character Sketch Write a character sketch of Nell Fossey that tracks her character traits, motivations, and feelings.

Responses will vary but should include a narrative paragraph that shows Nell's character traits, motivations, and feelings.

Conventions

Form Regular Past Tense Verbs

DIRECTIONS Write the correct form of the verb on each line.

Verb	Present Tense		Past Tense
	no ending	add ending: -s	add ending: -ed
to earn	I **earn**	He **earns**	They **earned**
to slip	I **slip**	He **slips**	They **slipped**
to glance	I **glance**	He **glances**	They **glanced**

Students write routinely for a range of tasks, purposes, and audiences. Students practice various conventions of standard English.

Name ____________________

Plurals *-s, -es, -ies*

DIRECTIONS Use the plural form of each word in ( ) to complete each sentence. Write the word on the line.

1. Samuel put his hands into his (pocket). **pockets**
2. He pulled out a handful of (penny). **pennies**
3. He also found ten (dollar). **dollars**
4. He used the money to buy three (paintbrush). **paintbrushes**
5. Later, Samuel squeezed paint from several (tube). **tubes**
6. He sketched a row of (box). **boxes**
7. In each one, he painted five (pansy). **pansies**
8. Each pansy had five (petal). **petals**
9. The finished painting measured 48 (inch). **inches**
10. Samuel gave it to his two best (friend). **friends**

DIRECTIONS Write the plural form of each word.

11. lady **ladies**
12. dish **dishes**
13. glass **glasses**
14. pose **poses**
15. book **books**
16. supply **supplies**
17. wax **waxes**
18. itch **itches**
19. daisy **daisies**
20. rock **rocks**

Students apply grade-level phonics and word analysis skills.

Benchmark Vocabulary

Name ________________________________

DIRECTIONS Write a sentence using each word.

confirmed naturalist

Responses should show contextual understanding of the word.

Write in Response to Reading

Read the fourth paragraph on p. 20 of *The Case of the Gasping Garbage*. The narrator makes statements about Nell Fossey. Do you agree with these statements? State your opinion and support it using text evidence.

Responses should use evidence from the text.

Students demonstrate contextual understanding of Benchmark Vocabulary. Students read text closely and use text evidence in their written answers.

Name ______________________

Writing

Establish a Situation Continue with the narrative you began in Lesson 4 by describing an event that introduces a problem.

Responses will vary but should include an event that introduces a problem to the narrative begun in Lesson 4.

Conventions

Form and Use Simple Verb Tenses

DIRECTIONS Form the past tense, present tense, and future tense of the following verbs:

1. talk **talked, talk, will talk**
2. jump **jumped, jump, will jump**
3. crawl **crawled, crawl, will crawl**

Students write routinely for a range of tasks, purposes, and audiences. Students practice various conventions of standard English.

Benchmark Vocabulary

Name ______________________________

DIRECTIONS Write a sentence using each word.

pollution habitat

Responses should show contextual understanding of the word.

Write in Response to Reading

How would you describe Drake's and Nell's motivations and actions? What do they do to show motivation? Use an example from the text to support your answer.

Responses should use evidence from the text. Their actions included Nell going on the radio, Drake calling all their friends to listen, and Nell organizing a rally that evening to accept donations to build a culvert. Their motivation was to save the frogs.

Students demonstrate contextual understanding of Benchmark Vocabulary. Students read text closely and use text evidence in their written answers.

Name ______________________

Writing

Write a Series of Events in Order Continue with the narrative you began in Lessons 4 and 6 by writing a series of events that seem to unfold naturally. First, list a series of events. Then, put them in a logical order.

Responses will vary but should include a series of events in a logical order.

Conventions

Form Simple Sentences Using Regular Verbs

DIRECTIONS Write two simple sentences that use regular verbs.

Laura likes her new bike.

Jeremiah played basketball.

Students write routinely for a range of tasks, purposes, and audiences. Students practice various conventions of standard English.

Benchmark Vocabulary

Name ______________________________

DIRECTIONS Write a sentence using each word.

desperate situation stumped archrival analysis

Responses should show contextual understanding of the word.

Write in Response to Reading

Read the paragraph on p. 32 of *The Case of the Gasping Garbage* that begins "This is a chance for Doyle and Fossey." Write a brief narrative in which you retell this part of the story from Frisco's perspective.

Responses will vary but should use evidence from the text, including that Frisco believed he was a better scientist than Doyle and Fossey. He thought he could solve the problem before them because he could go wherever he wanted since his father was the police commissioner.

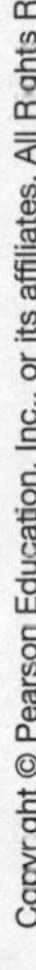

Students demonstrate contextual understanding of Benchmark Vocabulary. Students read text closely and use text evidence in their written answers.

Name ____

Sequence of Events

DIRECTIONS Using evidence from the text, answer the following questions about Chapter 5 from *The Case of the Gasping Garbage.*

1. What is the sequence, or order, of events?

Drake calls Nell to tell her about the accident, they go to the site, Nell shows her card so they can enter the scene, they measure and calculate, Nell stays at the site, and Drake goes to the lab.

2. What does Nell do to affect these events? What does Drake do to affect these events?

Nell shows her card and the two are allowed to pass; Drake suggests raising the bridge using hot-air balloons. He also alerts the two to the news on TV.

3. Compare and contrast the effect of Drake's actions and Nell's actions on the sequence of events.

Responses should use evidence from the text, including that they both calculated but Nell stays at the site and Drake goes to the lab. Students might also mention that Drake comes up with an idea quickly.

4. What are the most important events in Chapter 5? Why are they important?

Drake's suggestion and Nell's decision to stay behind are the most important events in Chapter 5. Drake thinks he can solve the case. Nell thinks there might be a better way to solve the case.

Students analyze and respond to literary and informational text.

Name ______________________________

Use Temporal Words and Phrases Write a one-paragraph narrative using the events you listed in Lesson 7. Use temporal (time order) words or phrases to begin the event sequence, to signal the order of events, and to end the event sequence.

Responses should include logically ordered events.

Form Simple Sentences with Nouns, Verbs, and Temporal Words

DIRECTIONS Form three simple sentences using a noun, a verb, and a temporal word or phrase.

First, Theodore made pancakes.

Lydia went home after she left the library.

Now, we will read the chapter together.

Students write routinely for a range of tasks, purposes, and audiences. Students practice various conventions of standard English.

Benchmark Vocabulary

Name ______________________________

DIRECTIONS Write a sentence using each word.

surveyed deflate

Responses should show contextual understanding of the word.

Write in Response to Reading

Read the third paragraph on p. 43 of *The Case of the Gasping Garbage*. The narrator states that Nell's tadpoles were glad to see her. Describe Nell's experience when she finally got home.

Responses may vary but from text evidence we can infer that she was tired.

Students demonstrate contextual understanding of Benchmark Vocabulary. Students read text closely and use text evidence in their written answers.

Name ______________________________

Write a Dialogue Write a dialogue between two characters that develops their experiences. Make sure the dialogue sounds like two real people are talking.

Responses will vary but should include a dialogue between two characters that develops character experiences.

Use Quotation Marks in Dialogue

DIRECTIONS Use quotation marks to separate the dialogue from the description.

1. "Where did you get that from?" asked Joe.
2. Mother said, "I want you to come home for dinner."
3. "Don't forget your scarf!" yelled Lauren.

Students write routinely for a range of tasks, purposes, and audiences. Students practice various conventions of standard English.

Benchmark Vocabulary

Name ______________________________

DIRECTIONS Write a sentence using each word.

anonymous suspended

Responses should show contextual understanding of the word.

Write in Response to Reading

Read p. 50 of *The Case of the Gasping Garbage.* How might you have gone about your investigation differently than Drake and Nell went about their investigation? State your opinion and support it using text evidence.

Responses should use evidence from the text.

Students demonstrate contextual understanding of Benchmark Vocabulary. Students read text closely and use text evidence in their written answers.

Name ______________________________

Point of View

DIRECTIONS Using evidence from the text, answer the following questions about p. 45 from *The Case of the Gasping Garbage.*

1. What is Drake's point of view about cases involving love?

   Drake does not like to take cases involving love because it cannot be measured.

2. Would you take a case that involves love? Explain your answer.

   Responses will vary.

3. How does Lilly feel about finding the person who wrote her a love letter?

   Lilly is eager to find out who wrote her the love letter.

4. What evidence supports your answer?

   When Lilly calls Drake, she tells him that she is desperate to find out who sent her the love letter. This shows how badly she wants to find out who wrote the letter.

5. How would you feel about finding the person who wrote you a love letter? Explain your answer.

   Responses will vary.

Students analyze and respond to literary and informational text.

Name ______________________

Writing

Write a Dialogue For one of the characters in the narrative you have been working on, write a dialogue that reveals his or her response to a situation.

Responses will vary but should include a dialogue between at least two characters that shows how one character responds to a situation.

Conventions

Use Commas in Dialogue

DIRECTIONS Insert commas into the dialogue.

1. "I am tired," Evan said.
2. The detective thought, "I can solve anything!"
3. "Let's go to the mall," replied Debra.

Students write routinely for a range of tasks, purposes, and audiences. Students practice various conventions of standard English.

Name ______________________________

Base Words and Endings

DIRECTIONS Add ***-ed*** and ***-ing*** to each word on the left. Remember that you may have to double the last consonant or drop the final *e*.

Word	-ed	-ing
plan	**planned**	**planning**
1. please	pleased	pleasing
2. close	closed	closing
3. shop	shopped	shopping
4. tire	tired	tiring
5. tug	tugged	tugging

DIRECTIONS Add ***-er*** and ***-est*** to each word on the left. Remember that you may have to double the last consonant, drop the final *e*, or change *y* to *i*.

Word	-er	-est
heavy	**heavier**	**heaviest**
6. soft	softer	softest
7. easy	easier	easiest
8. thin	thinner	thinnest
9. fluffy	fluffier	fluffiest
10. sore	sorer	sorest

Students apply grade-level phonics and word analysis skills.

Benchmark Vocabulary

Name ______________________________

DIRECTIONS Write a sentence using the word.

elementary

Responses should show contextual understanding of the word.

Write in Response to Reading

Skim through Chapter 8 of *The Case of the Gasping Garbage* to remind yourself of its main points. On a separate sheet of paper, write a short narrative that describes what Lilly does after she finds out who wrote the love letter. Keep in mind that characters' actions impact the sequence of events in a story.

Responses should use evidence from the text, including that Lilly was silent and then slipped to the floor, said Baloney's name, told Drake and Nell that it was the happiest day of her life, and gave them each a tiny hug. She then flew out of the room.

Students demonstrate contextual understanding of Benchmark Vocabulary. Students read text closely and use text evidence in their written answers.

Writing

Name ______________________________

Use Description to Develop Experiences Write a narrative that uses description to develop a character's experience. Describe an action, a thought, or a feeling using descriptive details.

Responses may vary but should include a description of a character's action, thought, or feeling that develops the character's experience.

Conventions

How Nouns Function in a Sentence

DIRECTIONS Circle the subject, and underline the direct object in each sentence.

1. The batter hit the ball.
2. The man built a house.
3. The dog is eating its food.

Students write routinely for a range of tasks, purposes, and audiences. Students practice various conventions of standard English.

Benchmark Vocabulary

Name ______________________________

DIRECTIONS Write a sentence using each word.

solution observations hypothesis

Responses should show contextual understanding of the word.

Write in Response to Reading

Read pp. 16–17 in *The Case of the Gasping Garbage* and pp. 37–39 in "Location, Location, Location." Compare and contrast the way Drake, Nell, and Evan identify problems and find solutions. Support your answers using text evidence.

Responses should use evidence from the text, including that Drake and Nell measure, experiment, and test their hypothesis about the problem. At this point in the story, Evan tries to convince Officer Ken to let him stay in the town green by explaining why he needs to win the competition against his sister. Both Drake and Nell and Evan talk through their problems, but Drake and Nell also use the scientific method. Drake and Nell are successful in finding the answer but Evan is not successful in staying in his spot.

Students demonstrate contextual understanding of Benchmark Vocabulary. Students read text closely and use text evidence in their written answers.

Name ______________________________

Sequence of Events

DIRECTIONS Using evidence from the text, answer the following questions about *The Case of the Gasping Garbage* and "Location, Location, Location."

1. In "Location, Location, Location," what decision does Evan make after he hears how much the lemonade costs in the ice cream shop? What happens after he makes this decision?

   Evan decides to sell his lemonade at a cheaper price—two dollars—and he gets a lot of customers.

2. What happens to Evan's lemonade stand because of his decision to sell lemonade in the town center?

   Officer Ken shuts his lemonade stand down because he does not have a permit to sell his lemonade in the town center.

3. In *The Case of the Gasping Garbage*, how does Drake respond when Gabby threatens to call Frisco? Why does he respond this way?

   Drake says that he will come right over. He does not want Frisco to take the case because he thinks Frisco is a bad scientist.

4. Why does Drake decide not to open Gabby's garbage can? What do Drake and Nell do instead to help them solve the case?

   Drake decides not to open the garbage can because there might be a monster inside. Drake and Nell make observations, take notes, draw diagrams and charts, and ask Gabby questions.

Students analyze and respond to literary and informational text.

Name ______________________

Writing

Use Description to Show Responses Write a paragraph that describes the response of a character to a situation. Conclude with a sentence describing what will happen next.

Responses will vary but should include a character's response to a situation and a description of what will occur next.

Conventions

Form and Use Irregular Plural Nouns

DIRECTIONS Use the plural of each noun in a sentence.

1. foot **Norma had very small feet.**
2. man **The men removed their hats.**
3. leaf **The tree's leaves had fallen to the ground.**
4. mouse **The mice ran under the bin.**
5. child **The children did not hear the bell.**

Students write routinely for a range of tasks, purposes, and audiences. Students practice various conventions of standard English.

Name ______________________________

DIRECTIONS Write a sentence using each word.

overcome horizon squinted luscious

Responses should show contextual understanding of the word.

Read p. 12 of *Thunder Cake.* The narrator says she was scared while walking through Tangleweed Woods to collect the ingredients from the dry shed. Why do you think she was scared? State your opinion and support it using text evidence.

Responses should use evidence from the text, including that the storm was coming and there was thunder and lightning. Students might also mention that she was scared of other things also, such as the Kick Cow.

Students demonstrate contextual understanding of Benchmark Vocabulary. Students read text closely and use text evidence in their written answers.

Name ______________________________________

Sleuth Work

Lin's Lesson

"You know you're not supposed to bring food downstairs," Mom said to Lin. She was walking up the stairs from Lin's bedroom holding a plate of dried-up sandwich. "When you leave food out, bugs come, and I can't stand bugs. If you want a snack, eat it upstairs."

"Yes, Mom," Lin said, only half paying attention. He didn't see what the big deal was and why she was so worried about bugs. The few he'd seen in his room were harmless little ants. Sometimes when he was drawing, he got so preoccupied that he forgot about the snacks he had brought downstairs.

The next morning, Lin woke up to a strange sensation. He opened his eyes and saw ants crawling over his arm. Lin bolted out of bed. Ants were crawling on the floor and in and out of the pretzel bag that was open on his desk. Lin ran upstairs, where he found his mom drinking her morning cup of tea.

"Mom!" Lin howled. "There are ants all over my room, even in my bed! I never thought this would happen!"

"Oh, Lin," Mom replied, "that's why we have rules—to avoid just this kind of thing. I'll have to call the exterminator, and you'll have to save your allowance and pay me back. Got it?"

"Yes, Mom. I'm really sorry." Lin had learned his lesson the hard way! He would have to use his own money to pay to get the ants removed.

Students read text closely to determine what the text says.

Sleuth Work

Name ____________________

Gather Evidence Circle 3 details from "Lin's Lesson" to support whether or not Lin learns his lesson. In another color, circle the detail that best supports whether Lin learns his lesson. **Responses will vary.**

Gather Evidence: Extend Your Ideas Briefly explain why the circled details are important to the story. Then work with a partner, and discuss how changing just one of these details would affect the story.

Responses should use evidence from the text.

Ask Questions Write two questions you think Lin and his mother would ask each other about this experience a week after it happened. Underline any words that could help answer the first question. Underline twice any words that could help answer the second question.

Responses should use evidence from the text.

Ask Questions: Extend Your Ideas Did you underline any answers in the text? If the answer is yes, explain. If the answer is no, write another question that the text answers and the answer from the text below.

Responses should use evidence from the text.

Make Your Case Choose either Lin or his mother. Circle 3–4 details the writer includes to show how the character feels. **Responses will vary.**

Make Your Case: Extend Your Ideas Write 1–2 sentences explaining how essential Lin's or his mother's feelings are to the story. How would the story be different if their feelings were exchanged?

Responses should use evidence from the text.

Students read text closely to determine what the text says.

Name ______________________________

Writing

Provide a Sense of Closure On a separate sheet of paper, write a brief narrative that introduces a character and a problem, explains the character's solution to the problem, and provides a sense of closure.

Responses may vary but should include a brief narrative that provides a sense of closure.

Conventions

Identify the Functions of Verbs

DIRECTIONS Identify the verb and function of the verb in the following sentences:

1. The man was tall. **was, state of being**

2. Grandma looked at the horizon. **looked, action**

3. Kelly walks to the store every week. **walks, action**

Students write routinely for a range of tasks, purposes, and audiences. Students practice various conventions of standard English.

Benchmark Vocabulary

Name ______________________

DIRECTIONS Write a sentence using each word.

overcome horizon

Responses should show contextual understanding of the word.

Write in Response to Reading

Read p. 5 of *Thunder Cake*. This introduction is told from the granddaughter's point of view. Retell the introduction to *Thunder Cake* from Grandma's point of view.

Responses will vary but should include text evidence such as information about the storm and Grandma's history, and how Grandma helped her granddaughter overcome her fear of storms.

Students demonstrate contextual understanding of Benchmark Vocabulary. Students read text closely and use text evidence in their written answers.

Name ______________________

Words That Create Effect

DIRECTIONS Using evidence from the text, answer the following questions about *Thunder Cake*.

1. Read p. 5 of *Thunder Cake*. What are some words the author uses to describe the characters or setting?

   sultry, damp, heavy, sharp, crackling, little, etc.

2. Explain how the author uses these descriptive details to develop the setting.

   The author uses these descriptive words to set the tone of the story.

3. What effect do these details have on the story?

   The effect is scary.

4. Read the sentences on p. 17 of *Thunder Cake*. How does the author use descriptive details to develop Grandma's character?

   Her voice was steady and soft.

5. What effect do these words and phrases have on the story?

   Her character is steady and reassuring, which helps her granddaughter overcome her fear.

Students analyze and respond to literary and informational text.

Writing

Name ______________________________

Plan and Prewrite Plan a story similar to *Thunder Cake* in which you write about a time when fear turned into courage.

Responses may vary.

Conventions

Identify Forms of Irregular Verbs

DIRECTIONS Underline the irregular verb in each sentence.

1. Florence walked back to her house because she had forgotten her bag.
2. Wallace understood that he could not talk loudly in the library.
3. Gloria fixed the flat tire and drove home.

Students write routinely for a range of tasks, purposes, and audiences. Students practice various conventions of standard English.

Benchmark Vocabulary

Name ____________________

DIRECTIONS Write a sentence using each word.

squinted luscious

Responses should show contextual understanding of the word.

Write in Response to Reading

Read pp. 5–8 of *Thunder Cake*. Write a sentence or two explaining why Grandma chose to bake a Thunder Cake. Use text evidence to support your explanation.

Responses should use evidence from the text, such as she may have been trying to help her granddaughter overcome her fear of storms by having her help bake the cake.

Students demonstrate contextual understanding of Benchmark Vocabulary. Students read text closely and use text evidence in their written answers.

Name ____________________

Draft Draft the story you planned in Lesson 14 on a separate sheet of paper.

Responses may vary but should include a draft of a story.

Verbs That End in *-y*

DIRECTIONS Rewrite the following sentences using the verbs in the past tense:

1. Nell hurries to campus. **Nell hurried to campus.**

2. The pirates bury treasure. **The pirates buried treasure.**

3. Gregory will study for the test. **Gregory studied for the test.**

Students write routinely for a range of tasks, purposes, and audiences. Students practice various conventions of standard English.

Name ______________________

Phonics

Vowel Digraphs *ee, ea, ai, ay, oa, ow*

DIRECTIONS Choose the word with the **long a, long e,** or **long o** sound that best matches each definition. Write the word on the line.

1. all right	okay	glad	okay	well
2. winter garment	coat	hat	boot	coat
3. free of dirt	clean	clean	fresh	spotless
4. toss	throw	pitch	lob	throw
5. go along	agree	admit	agree	settle
6. lift up	raise	raise	heft	build
7. warm up	toast	cook	toast	broil
8. remain	stay	stay	last	linger
9. type of grass	reed	moss	reed	straw

DIRECTIONS Circle the word that has the **long a, long e,** or **long o** sound. Then underline the letters in the word that stand for that vowel sound.

10. crop	clock	creek
11. belt	below	bought
12. latch	float	bread
13. braid	bride	brook
14. feast	flash	frost
15. stray	struck	stop

Students apply grade-level phonics and word analysis skills.

Benchmark Vocabulary

Name ______________________________

DIRECTIONS Write a sentence using each word.

observations situation

Responses should show contextual understanding of the word.

Write in Response to Reading

Read p. 18 in *The Case of the Gasping Garbage* from "It was Friday after school . . . " to "Mrs. Doyle closed the door." Then read pp. 6–7 in *Thunder Cake* from "'Steady child . . . '" to "'Thunder Cake?' I stammered as I hugged her even closer." Which text do you think uses narrative techniques more effectively? State your opinion. Then support your opinion with reasons and evidence from the text.

Responses should use evidence from the text.

Students demonstrate contextual understanding of Benchmark Vocabulary. Students read text closely and use text evidence in their written answers.

Name ______________________________

Writing

Revise On a separate sheet of paper, revise the narrative you drafted in Lesson 15. Look for areas where you can add details and descriptive language to make your story more interesting and areas where you can add appropriate dialogue. Make sure that the end resolves the problem in your story.

Responses may vary but should revise the narrative from Lesson 15 so that it includes descriptive language, dialogue, and a solution to the story's problem.

Conventions

Use Irregular Verbs in Sentences

DIRECTIONS For each verb below, write one sentence that uses the verb in the present tense, one sentence that uses the verb in the past tense, and one sentence that uses the verb's past participle.

1. become

I become nervous when the teacher calls on me. They became scientists and conducted many experiments. We have become just like our parents.

2. shake

She shakes the salad dressing before putting it on her salad. You shook your head. They have shaken the cans of paint.

Students write routinely for a range of tasks, purposes, and audiences. Students practice various conventions of standard English.

Benchmark Vocabulary

Name ______________________________

DIRECTIONS Write a sentence using each word.

location earned competition

Responses should show contextual understanding of the word.

Write in Response to Reading

Read p. 31 from "He needed a plan" to "He just needed to find something with wheels to get him there" in "Location, Location, Location." Then read pp. 6–7 of *Thunder Cake* from "The air was hot, heavy and damp" to "'Thunder Cake?' I stammered as I hugged her even closer." Compare and contrast the way Grandma and Evan identify problems and find solutions. Support your answers using text evidence.

Responses should use evidence from the text. Both Evan and Grandma see a problem and try to solve it. Evan envisions something he wants ("thirsty people, all waving dollar bills at him") and tries to find a way to make that happen. Grandma sees that the child is afraid of the storm. Grandma helps the child by having her face her fears and help bake a Thunder Cake.

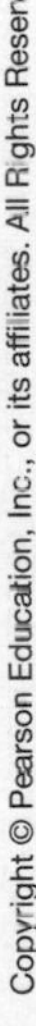

Students demonstrate contextual understanding of Benchmark Vocabulary. Students read text closely and use text evidence in their written answers.

Name ______________________

Compare Narratives

DIRECTIONS Using evidence from the texts, answer the following questions about "Location, Location, Location" and *Thunder Cake*.

1. Describe how Evan identifies problems and finds solutions.

   Responses should use evidence from the text, including that Evan determines what he needs to do to beat Jess (the problem) and how he can do that by selling $53 of lemonade (the solution).

2. Describe how Grandma identifies problems and finds solutions.

   Responses should use evidence from the text, including that Grandma sees the scared child hiding under the bed (the problem) and has her come out to help make a Thunder Cake (the solution).

3. How is Evan's process for identifying problems and finding solutions different from Grandma's process? **Evan imagines what he needs to beat Jess, which leads him to the solution. Grandma sees the child is afraid and creates a solution by having her do scary things and then praising her. Evan works alone; Grandma helps the child.**

4. How is it similar to Grandma's process?

   Both Evan and Grandma work through a series of steps to accomplish their solutions.

Students analyze and respond to literary and informational text.

Writing

Name ______________________________

Edit Edit the story you began in Lesson 14. Write your edited story on a separate sheet of paper.

Responses may vary but should include edits to the revised narrative.

Conventions

Identify Pronouns

DIRECTIONS Underline the pronoun in each sentence.

1. Drake couldn't believe them.
2. He wanted to find a way for the frogs to cross the street safely.
3. She said the bandage was too tight.

Students write routinely for a range of tasks, purposes, and audiences. Students practice various conventions of standard English.

Benchmark Vocabulary

Name ____________________

DIRECTIONS Write a sentence using each word.

anonymous elementary

Responses should show contextual understanding of the word.

Write in Response to Reading

Read p. 18 in *The Case of the Gasping Garbage* from "It was Friday after school . . ." to "Mrs. Doyle closed the door." Then read p. 18 in *Thunder Cake* from "But you got out from under it" to "'From where I sit, only a very brave person could have done all them things!'" Finally, read p. 31 in "Location, Location, Location" from "It took Evan half an hour to drag his loaded wagon to the town center" to "But once he was there, he knew it was worth it." Compare and contrast the way in which one character from each text changes over time. Support your answers using text evidence.

Responses should use evidence from the text.

Students demonstrate contextual understanding of Benchmark Vocabulary. Students read text closely and use text evidence in their written answers.

Name ______________________________

Publish and Present Publish and present your narrative. Write the final version of your narrative on a separate sheet of paper.

Responses may vary but should include a narrative that has been published and presented.

Using Pronouns in Sentences

DIRECTIONS Circle the nouns in each sentence. Then write a pronoun that could replace each noun on the line below the sentence.

1. Drake and Nell can solve a problem by working in the lab or talking with friends.

   He, she, it, it, them

2. Grandma whispered as she squinted at the list.

   She, it

3. Evan decided to draw dollar signs.

   He, them

Students write routinely for a range of tasks, purposes, and audiences. Students practice various conventions of standard English.

Name ______________________________ Phonics

Vowel Digraphs *ee, ea, ai, ay, oa, ow*

DIRECTIONS Use context to help you complete each sentence with one or more words from the Word Bank. You will not use all of the words.

Word Bank

steal	float	rays	thrown	knees	shadow
coach	reached	lower	brain	away	between
straight	trait	feet	stay	road	bleachers

1. I saw that the catcher had **thrown** the ball to third base.
2. I decided to try to **steal** second base.
3. The ball seemed to **float** slowly through the air.
4. My **coach** yelled for me to **stay** on first.
5. However, I had already stepped **away** from the base.
6. My **brain** had already told my legs to run, so I went.
7. The fans in the **bleachers** yelled for me to run.
8. I was still **between** bases when my **feet** got tangled.
9. I was lucky—the catcher's throw went **straight** into the stands!
10. I **reached** third base, where I was safe.
11. I fell to my **knees** with relief.
12. The **rays** of bright sunlight must have blinded her.

DIRECTIONS Combine each word on the left with the word on the right that has the same long vowel sound. Write the new word on the line.

13. **railway** rail boat
14. **seaweed** sea way
15. **showboat** show weed

Students apply grade-level phonics and word analysis skills.

Benchmark Vocabulary

Name ______________________________

DIRECTIONS Write a sentence using each word.

quarter crescent waxing waning phases

Responses should show contextual understanding of the word.

Write in Response to Reading

Read p. 43 from *The Moon Seems to Change* and study the illustrations. According to the text, "the moon seems to change." How does the moon's appearance change over time?

Responses should use evidence from the text, including that after the full moon you see less and less of the moon and after the nights with no moon you see more and more of it.

Students demonstrate contextual understanding of Benchmark Vocabulary. Students read text closely and use text evidence in their written answers.

Writing

Name ______________________________

Convey Ideas and Information Write a paragraph that introduces a topic and uses facts to explain it. First, write a sentence that introduces and explains your topic. Then, list three facts and key details that support your topic.

Responses will vary but should include a paragraph that introduces a topic and three facts and key details that support the topic.

Conventions

Nouns as Subjects

DIRECTIONS Underline the noun that serves as the subject of each sentence.

1. Each night the crescent gets a bit thinner.
2. Spaceships went around the moon.
3. The sky is dark.

Students write routinely for a range of tasks, purposes, and audiences. Students practice various conventions of standard English.

Benchmark Vocabulary

Name ______________________________

DIRECTIONS Write a sentence using each word.

waxing waning

Responses should show contextual understanding of the word.

Write in Response to Reading

Read p. 55 from *The Moon Seems to Change*. Write a paragraph explaining how the phases of the moon cause the moon to seem to change. Be sure to support your explanation using details from the text.

Responses should use evidence from the text, including that when the new moon is between the Earth and the sun, we only see the dark half. As the moon moves around Earth, we see more of the lighted half until the moon is opposite the sun. This is the full moon, and we see the full lighted half. As the moon continues around the Earth, we see more of the dark half until the moon is again between the Earth and the sun. It is then a new moon again. This takes about four weeks.

Students demonstrate contextual understanding of Benchmark Vocabulary. Students read text closely and use text evidence in their written answers.

Name ______________________________

Text Features

DIRECTIONS Using evidence from the text, answer the following questions about pp. 46–53 of *The Moon Seems to Change*.

1. Look at the illustrations at the bottom of p. 48. What do they show?

   They show a person's view of a new moon during the day and at night.

2. How do they help the reader understand why the moon only *seems* to change?

   They show that the locations of the moon, Earth, and sun affect what a person sees and that the moon is not actually changing.

3. Look at the illustration at the bottom of p. 49. What does it show?

   It shows a child looking at the moon around sunset.

4. How does it help the reader understand why the moon only *seems* to change?

   It shows that the moon *seems* to change because it is visible at different times of the day during different phases.

Students analyze and respond to literary and informational text.

Name ______________________

Writing

Genre Write a paragraph that identifies the genre of the paragraph you wrote in Lesson 1 and explains the reasons you used to identify the paragraph's genre.

Responses will vary but should include a genre and the reasons the student used to identify that genre.

Conventions

Use a Noun as a Subject

DIRECTIONS For each noun below, write a sentence that uses the noun as a subject.

1. planet **The planet has no water.**
2. star **The star was very bright.**
3. day **The day passed quickly.**

Students write routinely for a range of tasks, purposes, and audiences. Students practice various conventions of standard English.

Benchmark Vocabulary

Name ________________________________

DIRECTIONS Write a sentence using each word.

quarter crescent phases

Responses should show contextual understanding of the word.

Write in Response to Reading

Read p. 50 of *The Moon Seems to Change*. Look at the illustrations and write about what you see. How do the illustrations help you understand the text? Support your response with evidence from the text.

Responses should include that the illustration at the top shows that as the moon moves between the Earth and the sun we can see more of the lighted half of the moon, so it looks like it is growing. The bottom illustration shows the shape of the whole moon and how much of the moon is lighted.

Students demonstrate contextual understanding of Benchmark Vocabulary. Students read text closely and use text evidence in their written answers.

Name ____

A Whale of a Rescue

Imagine walking along the beach and stopping now and then to pick up an interesting shell. You see something at the water's edge. You realize it's a whale—a whale stranded on the beach.

Some animals, such as seals, often come out of the water onto the shore. But for whales, dolphins, and porpoises, this behavior usually means that something is wrong. Sometimes the animal is sick, but sometimes it has just lost its way. Swimming in stormy seas can exhaust some animals. Their exhaustion will make them disoriented. Others get stuck in shallow waters when the tide is outgoing.

One time, in February 2011, not just one whale, but 82 were stranded! For reasons unknown, 82 pilot whales became stranded on a beach in New Zealand.

The Department of Conservation of New Zealand, along with over 100 volunteers, came to the rescue. They worked all weekend long to get the animals back into the water. All but 17 whales made it.

Then, just days later, 65 whales were stranded again! This time, the volunteers didn't try to move the whales back into the water. "New evidence suggests that moving stranded whales causes them a lot of stress and pain," Department of Conservation ranger Simon Walls told a local newspaper. Instead, the volunteers cared for the whales on shore while waiting for the high tides to return.

All 65 of the newly stranded whales were successfully returned to the water. The plan had worked!

Students read text closely to determine what the text says.

Sleuth Work

Name ____________________________

Gather Evidence Underline 3–4 details in the text that explain why whales might become stranded on the beach.

See annotations on previous page.

Gather Evidence: Extend Your Ideas Work with a partner, and discuss how changing just one of these details would affect the text.

Responses will vary.

Ask Questions Write three questions about the stranded pilot whales and the people who tried to help them. Highlight words in the text that could help answer your first question. Bracket any words that could help answer your second question. Draw a box around any words that could help answer your third question.

Responses will vary but could include: Did the volunteers have training? What kind of whales were stranded? Were they the same kind of whales both times?

Ask Questions: Extend Your Ideas Did you mark any words in the text that would answer your questions? If the answer is yes, explain. If the answer is no, write another question that the text answers and the answer from the text below.

Responses will vary.

Make Your Case Circle words in the text that the author uses to compare and contrast the two events in the text.

See annotations on previous page.

Make Your Case: Extend Your Ideas Write 2–3 sentences comparing and contrasting the two events. Sample response: Whales were stranded in New Zealand twice in 2011. Both times volunteers worked to save the whales, but the second time the volunteers just waited until high tide. Seventeen whales died the first time they were stranded on the beach, but all the whales survived during second time.

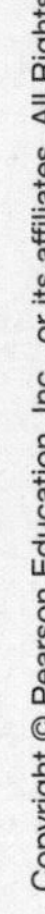

Students read text closely to determine what the text says.

Name ______________________________

Use Illustrations to Convey Information Review the paragraph you wrote for Lesson 1. Decide which fact or facts could be better explained in an illustration or diagram. Draw the illustration or diagram below or on a separate sheet of paper.

Responses will vary but should include an illustration that conveys a fact or facts that can be better expressed as an illustration.

Subject-Verb Agreement: Past Tense

DIRECTIONS Write the correct past-tense form of the verb *be* in each sentence.

1. The cows **were** hungry.
2. I **was** very tired last night.
3. You **were** my best friend.

Students write routinely for a range of tasks, purposes, and audiences. Students practice various conventions of standard English.

Benchmark Vocabulary

Name ______________________________

DIRECTIONS Write a sentence using each word.

gnarled scowls

Responses should show contextual understanding of the word.

Write in Response to Reading

Read p. 8 of *Treasure in the Trees*. How do Nisha's parents view the success of their shop? How do you view the success of their shop? Support your answer with evidence from the text.

Responses will vary but should include that Nisha's dad is worried about the shop and says they may "have bitten off more than we can chew." Nisha's mom is also worried but seems more hopeful because she says, "It will all be fine." Student opinions should be supported with evidence from the text.

Students demonstrate contextual understanding of Benchmark Vocabulary. Students read text closely and use text evidence in their written answers.

Name ______________________________

Point of View

DIRECTIONS Using evidence from the text, answer the following questions about pp. 6–7 of *Treasure in the Trees.*

1. How do Nisha's parents feel about her changing an image of her grandparents? What evidence from the text supports your answer?

   Nisha's parents did not think the image was funny. The text says they would not let her use the computer for a week, which shows that they think she did something wrong.

2. How do you feel about Nisha changing an image of her grandparents?

   Responses will vary.

3. How does Nisha feel about convincing her parents to save the tree? What evidencc from the text supports your answer?

   Nisha seems determined to convince her parents to save the tree. In the text, she talks about showing them scientific evidence and showing them her secret so that they will believe her.

4. How do you think Nisha should feel about convincing her parents to save the tree?

   Responses will vary.

Students analyze and respond to literary and informational text.

Writing

Name ______________________________

Introduce a Topic Decide what the topic and main idea of your informative/explanatory text will be. Then write one or two sentences that introduce the topic and one or two sentences that state your main idea.

Responses will vary but should include an introductory paragraph with one or two sentences that introduce the topic and one or two sentences that introduce the main idea.

Conventions

Subject-Verb Agreement: Past Tense

DIRECTIONS Complete each sentence with the past-tense form of the verb.

1. Tina **decided** (decide) to tell her best friend her secret.
2. Her parents **were** (be) always tired after working at the hotel.
3. We **played** (play) with our turtle, Scooter.

Students write routinely for a range of tasks, purposes, and audiences. Students practice various conventions of standard English.

Benchmark Vocabulary

Name ______________________________

DIRECTIONS Write a sentence using each word.

exasperated grove frustrated underside

Responses should show contextual understanding of the word.

Write in Response to Reading

Reread the last paragraph on p. 13. How does the sentence structure help communicate a change in Nisha's attention?

Responses should mention that it is a long, compound sentence. The beginning of the sentence seems rushed as Nisha is frustrated. The second part of the sentence slows down to more descriptive, thoughtful language.

Students demonstrate contextual understanding of Benchmark Vocabulary. Students read text closely and use text evidence in their written answers.

Writing

Name ________________________________

Group Related Information Reread the introductory paragraph you wrote in Lesson 4. Gather and group information related to your topic. Then write it below. Look for ways the groups of information can suggest sub-ideas or key details for your essay.

Responses will vary but should include grouped information related to the student's topic.

Conventions

Produce Simple Sentences

DIRECTIONS Write three simple sentences. One sentence should have two subjects, and one sentence should have two verbs.

Melissa talked with her friends.

The flowers and the tall grass swayed in the wind.

Our sister brushes her teeth and washes her face every night.

Students write routinely for a range of tasks, purposes, and audiences. Students practice various conventions of standard English.

Name ___________________________

Vowel Diphthongs *ou, ow, oi, oy*

DIRECTIONS Circle each word with **ou** or **ow** that has the same vowel sound as **out**. Then write the word or words on the line.

counted **1.** Jen slowly counted her money.

amount **2.** She had the amount she needed.

proud **3.** Jen was proud that she had earned enough.

Now, flowers **4.** Now she could buy flowers for her mother's show.

aloud **5.** "Good going!" she said aloud.

DIRECTIONS Circle each word with **oi** or **oy** that has the same vowel sound as **toy**. Then write the word or words on the line.

choice **6.** It was time for Ivan to make a choice.

employer **7.** Should he find a new employer?

noise, annoyed **8.** Here, the noise really annoyed him.

enjoy **9.** He just wanted to enjoy his job.

noisy, spoiled **10.** His noisy coworkers spoiled everything.

DIRECTIONS Circle each word with the same vowel sound as the first word. Then underline the letters in the circled word that stand for that vowel sound.

11. town	loyal	proud	snow
12. joy	sound	know	broil
13. voice	vote	plow	soil
14. hour	crown	float	show
15. join	bay	annoy	brown

Students apply grade-level phonics and word analysis skills.

Benchmark Vocabulary

Name ______________________________

DIRECTIONS Write a sentence using each word.

urged creature destroyed

Responses should show contextual understanding of the word.

Write in Response to Reading

Read p. 15 of *Treasure in the Trees*. How have Nisha's parents changed? Use evidence from the text to support your answer.

Responses should use evidence from the text, including that her parents were acting strangely and looked happier.

Students demonstrate contextual understanding of Benchmark Vocabulary. Students read text closely and use text evidence in their written answers.

Name ______________________________

Analyze Character

DIRECTIONS Using evidence from the text, answer the following questions about pp. 18–19 of *Treasure in the Trees*.

1. What does Nisha's father think of her observation about the curled leaves in the tree?

   Nisha's father thinks that Nisha is mistaken about what she has seen.

2. What evidence from the text supports your answer?

   Responses may vary but could include Nisha's father saying "And besides...the leaves are too high up to see clearly. Maybe it was just the light playing tricks on your eyes."

3. How does Nisha feel about her parents' response to seeing the curled leaves in the tree?

   She is disappointed that they do not believe there is something there.

4. What evidence from the text supports your answer?

   Responses may vary but could include that the narrator says that "Nisha's heart sank."

Students analyze and respond to literary and informational text.

Name ______________________________

Writing

Use Linking Words and Phrases to Connect Ideas On a separate sheet of paper, write several paragraphs that organize and develop the related ideas and details you grouped in Lesson 5. Use linking words and phrases to connect the ideas and details in your paragraphs.

Responses will vary but should include several paragraphs that use linking words and phrases to connect related ideas and details.

Conventions

Subject-Verb Agreement: Present Tense

DIRECTIONS Fill in each blank with the present-tense form of the verb that agrees with the subject of the sentence.

1. Crystal's dog **is** (be) small.
2. Her grandmother **cooks** (cook) dinner.
3. "We **are** (be) very tired," her mother said.

Students write routinely for a range of tasks, purposes, and audiences. Students practice various conventions of standard English.

Benchmark Vocabulary

Name ______________________________

DIRECTIONS Write a sentence using each word.

unfurled hastily rumbling desperately

Responses should show contextual understanding of the word.

Write in Response to Reading

Look at the illustration on p. 20 of *Treasure in the Trees.* What details from the text does the illustration show? How does it contribute to the story?

Responses should use evidence from the text, including Nisha carrying her notebook and pencils and marching to the tree, and Scruggs following her excitedly.

Students demonstrate contextual understanding of Benchmark Vocabulary. Students read text closely and use text evidence in their written answers.

Name ______________________________

Writing

Use Linking Words and Phrases to Compare Ideas On a separate sheet of paper, write several paragraphs that organize and develop the related ideas you grouped in Lesson 5. Use linking words and phrases to connect the ideas by comparing and contrasting them.

Responses will vary but should include ideas from Lesson 5 and compare and contrast them using linking words and phrases.

Conventions

Subject-Verb Agreement: Present Tense

DIRECTIONS Complete each sentence with the present-tense form of the verb.

1. Theresa **worries** (worry) about her little brother.
2. It **glides** (glide) through the water.
3. He **watches** (watch) the phone fall out of her pocket.

Students write routinely for a range of tasks, purposes, and audiences. Students practice various conventions of standard English.

Benchmark Vocabulary

Name ______________________________

DIRECTIONS Write a sentence using each word.

inched exclaimed creatures generous triumphantly

Responses should show contextual understanding of the word.

Write in Response to Reading

Read p. 31 of *Treasure in the Trees*. How do Nisha's parents respond when she shows them her notebook? Why do you think they respond this way? Use text evidence to support your answer.

Responses should use evidence from the text, including that they said she had an active imagination and didn't believe her. They may have responded that way because they got a very generous offer for the trees from the developers. Student opinions may vary.

Students demonstrate contextual understanding of Benchmark Vocabulary. Students read text closely and use text evidence in their written answers.

Name ______________________

Reading Analysis

Identifying and Explaining Key Events

DIRECTIONS Using evidence from the text, answer the following questions about pp. 30–33 of *Treasure in the Trees.*

1. What key event happens on p. 30? Why is this event important?

   Nisha actually sees the bugs curl up in the leaves. This is important because now she is certain of what is in the curled leaves.

2. What two key events happen on p. 31? Why are they important?

   Nisha's parents don't believe her when she shows them the notebook, and they tell her that the developers will be bringing the paperwork for selling the land the next day.

3. How do these two events affect Nisha's actions?

   These events make Nisha feel rushed to prove that there are bugs curled in the leaves of the tree, so she goes back to the grove to take pictures.

4. What key event happens on p. 33? Why is this event important?

   Nisha uploads her photos and sees that they are blurry. This event is important because she is running out of time and still does not have proof that there are bugs in the leaves.

Students analyze and respond to literary and informational text.

Writing

Name ______________________________

Develop the Topic Review the paragraphs you wrote in Lessons 6 and 7, looking for ideas that need more supporting facts or explanatory details and for unfamiliar terms that need to be defined. On a separate sheet of paper, add facts, definitions, and details to the paragraphs where needed.

Responses will vary but should expand on the paragraphs from Lessons 6 and 7.

Conventions

Subject-Verb Agreement: Future Tense

DIRECTIONS Complete each sentence with the future tense of the verb.

1. I **will run** (run) a mile tonight.
2. The teacher **will give** (give) us our assignment tomorrow.
3. His friends **will plan** (plan) a birthday party for him.

Students write routinely for a range of tasks, purposes, and audiences. Students practice various conventions of standard English.

Name ______________________

Benchmark Vocabulary

DIRECTIONS Write a sentence using each word.

fascinated unison amazing embraced

Responses should show contextual understanding of the word.

Write in Response to Reading

What lesson do you think Nisha's parents learn in Chapter 6 of *Treasure in the Trees*? Use evidence from the text to support your answer.

Responses should use evidence from the text, including that her parents were sorry they didn't believe her and that they realized she is a real scientist. Because of her discovery, they decide not to sell the grove. Students may also mention that the parents realize they were too busy with the shop.

Students demonstrate contextual understanding of Benchmark Vocabulary. Students read text closely and use text evidence in their written answers.

Name ________________________________

Draw an Illustration Look at your list of illustrations that might help you communicate the main ideas and key details in the piece of writing you began in Lesson 4. Draw one of those illustrations below or on a separate sheet of paper.

Responses will vary but should include an illustration that helps communicate a main idea or key detail.

Produce Simple Sentences Using Subject-Verb Agreement: Future Tense

DIRECTIONS Write two simple sentences, each with a verb in the future tense and correct subject-verb agreement.

Rebecca will write a letter to Jonah next week.

She and I will return the books to the library on Saturday.

Students write routinely for a range of tasks, purposes, and audiences. Students practice various conventions of standard English.

Name ______________________________

Benchmark Vocabulary

DIRECTIONS Write a sentence using each word.

planet liquid surrounds

Responses should show contextual understanding of the word.

Write in Response to Reading

Look at the photo of the astronaut on p. 5. How does it help you better understand gravity on Earth's moon?

Responses should use evidence from the text.

Students demonstrate contextual understanding of Benchmark Vocabulary. Students read text closely and use text evidence in their written answers.

Writing

Name ____

Write a Concluding Statement or Section Review the main ideas and supporting details in the piece of informative/explanatory writing that you began in Lesson 4. Think about the following questions:

1. What is interesting or important about your main idea?
2. Why would someone want or need to know about it?
3. Why does the topic of your essay matter?

Use your answers to these questions to help you write a concluding statement or section on a separate sheet of paper.

Responses will vary.

Conventions

Use Adjectives

DIRECTIONS Underline the adjective(s) in each sentence.

1. The huge bowl held sour candy.
2. My lazy cat likes to sleep on my soft blanket.
3. None of Delilah's tall friends like to ride in her small car.

Students write routinely for a range of tasks, purposes, and audiences. Students practice various conventions of standard English.

Name ________________________ **Phonics**

Syllable Patterns V/CV, VC/V

DIRECTIONS Circle each word in the box with the **long vowel** sound in the **first syllable**. Underline each word in the box with the **short vowel** sound in the **first syllable**. Then write each word in the correct column.

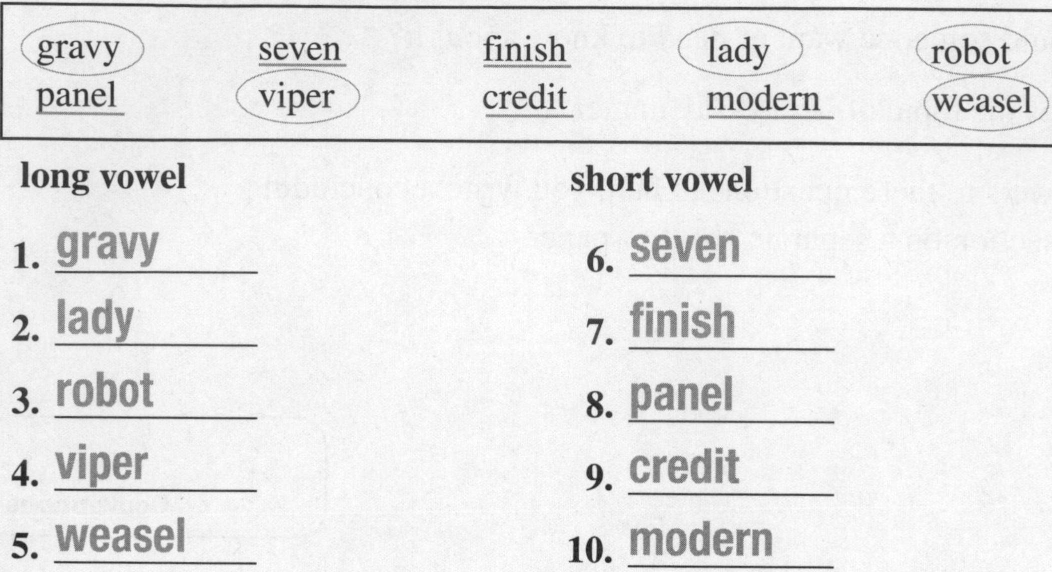

gravy	seven	finish	lady	robot
panel	viper	credit	modern	weasel

long vowel

1. gravy
2. lady
3. robot
4. viper
5. weasel

short vowel

6. seven
7. finish
8. panel
9. credit
10. modern

DIRECTIONS Cross out the words in the Word Bank that have a **short vowel** sound in the **first syllable**. Then complete the sentences with the words that have a **long vowel** sound in the **first syllable**.

Word Bank

~~cousin~~	chosen	~~pleasant~~	tiny	~~menu~~
raisins	~~honest~~	pupils	~~camels~~	reason

11. The normally quiet pupils began to shout.
12. Their teacher tried to figure out the reason.
13. He learned it once a spokesperson had been chosen.
14. The students were upset about tiny dots in the cereal.
15. None of them had ever seen raisins before!

Students apply grade-level phonics and word analysis skills.

Benchmark Vocabulary

Name ______________________________

DIRECTIONS Write a sentence using each word.

oceans contain streams

Responses should show contextual understanding of the word.

Write in Response to Reading

Why is the amount of water humans can drink limited even though 70% of Earth's surface is covered in water?

Responses should use evidence from the text, including that most of the water on Earth is salt water and humans cannot drink it.

Students demonstrate contextual understanding of Benchmark Vocabulary. Students read text closely and use text evidence in their written answers.

Name ______________________

Main Idea and Key Details

DIRECTIONS Using evidence from the text, answer the following questions about pp. 6–11 from *About Earth.*

1. How are lakes and oceans similar?

They are both sources of water on Earth.

2. How are lakes and oceans different?

Lakes are a source of fresh water, but oceans are not.

3. What would happen if all the ice on Earth melted? What does this tell you about Earth's water?

The seas would rise 230 feet, and many places would be flooded. This tells me that a lot of Earth's water is in the form of ice.

4. Where can you find fresh water?

You can find fresh water in lakes, rivers, streams, underground, or in ice.

Students analyze and respond to literary and informational text.

Name ______________________________

Present Review the written version of your informative/explanatory report. Write a paragraph describing the best way to present the material in a clear and interesting manner.

Responses will vary but should include ideas for presenting the student's report in a clear and interesting manner.

Use Articles as Adjectives

DIRECTIONS Write two sentences that use one or more of the following articles: *a, an,* and *the*. Circle the articles in your sentences.

A woman pushed a stroller across the street.

The lawyer walked into the courtroom with a large briefcase.

Students write routinely for a range of tasks, purposes, and audiences. Students practice various conventions of standard English.

Benchmark Vocabulary

Name ______________________________

DIRECTIONS Write a sentence using each word.

survive desert lizards

Responses should show contextual understanding of the word.

Write in Response to Reading

Look at the photograph of Antarctica on p. 12. How does the image help you understand the characteristics of dry places?

Responses should use evidence from the text, including that there are no plants in Antarctica.

Students demonstrate contextual understanding of Benchmark Vocabulary. Students read text closely and use text evidence in their written answers.

Name ______________________________

Plan and Prewrite Decide on a topic for an informational article. Gather information by talking to people, making observations, and reading about the topic. Take notes below or on a separate sheet of paper.

Responses will vary but should include notes about the information the student has gathered by talking to people, making observations, and reading about the topic he or she has chosen.

Form and Use Adjectives

DIRECTIONS Complete each sentence with the correct form of the adjective.

1. Jessie is the tallest (*tall,* superlative) girl in her family.
2. New Mexico is warmer (*warm*, comparative) than Massachusetts during the winter.
3. The oldest (*old*, superlative) person in the world is 117 years old.

Students write routinely for a range of tasks, purposes, and audiences. Students practice various conventions of standard English.

Benchmark Vocabulary

Name ______________________________

DIRECTIONS Write a sentence using each word.

sand grains   dunes   atmosphere   rainbow   scattered

Responses should show contextual understanding of the word.

Write in Response to Reading

Reread p. 16. How is sand formed? How do the photograph and caption at the bottom of the page help you understand that process?

Responses should use evidence from the text, including that rocks are broken by wind and water into smaller pieces to make sand. The photograph and caption help students understand the process because the water is wearing down the large rock.

Students demonstrate contextual understanding of Benchmark Vocabulary. Students read text closely and use text evidence in their written answers.

Name ______________________________

Backyard Safari

Because I live in the city, I rarely see animals that I read about in school. When Dad takes me to the park, I see pigeons and squirrels. Boring! I want to see snakes and rabbits.

Last weekend I stayed with Aunt Marie in the country. Instead of going to the park, I played in Aunt Marie's backyard.

When we arrived at Aunt Marie's, I found her fixing breakfast and wearing a strange hat. "What's that on your head?" I asked.

"It's my safari hat!" She held up a smaller one and tossed it to me. Aunt Marie explained that we were going on a backyard safari.

I inhaled my breakfast. Then we set out toward the yard with binoculars and a magnifying glass.

"Do you hear that?" Aunt Marie asked.

I heard what sounded like a tiny jackhammer. She handed me the binoculars and told me to look high up in the tree. I soon found the source of the noise. It was a woodpecker with a red head.

Aunt Marie said that rabbits love to rest under her rose bushes. We lay in the grass and waited. As we waited, she told me all about the critters that call her backyard home—opossum, raccoons, chipmunks, and snakes. Some like to come out early in the morning, others at night.

Then something caught my eye. It was a ball of fur with a nose that was wiggling. "A rabbit," I whispered, even though I wanted to yell. Who knew I could see so much wildlife on a backyard safari!

Students read text closely to determine what the text says.

Sleuth Work

Name ______________________________

Gather Evidence Circle two details in the text that show the narrator was excited about the backyard safari.

Responses may vary.

Gather Evidence: Extend Your Ideas Work with a partner, and discuss how changing just one of these details would affect the story.

Responses will vary.

Ask Questions Write two questions you would ask an expert about animals that live near humans. Underline any words in the text that could help answer the first question. Underline twice any words in the text that could help answer the second question.

Responses will vary.

Ask Questions: Extend Your Ideas Did you underline any words in the text that would answer your questions? If the answer is yes, explain. If the answer is no, write an additional question that is answered in the text, and include that answer with your new question on the lines below.

Responses will vary.

Make Your Case Circle words in the story that show how the narrator's home and Aunt Marie's home are alike and different.

Responses may vary.

Make Your Case: Extend Your Ideas Write a sentence or two explaining why the differences between their homes are important in the story.

Responses may vary.

Students read text closely to determine what the text says.

Name ______________________________

Draft On a separate sheet of paper, draft an article using the information you gathered in Lesson 12. Begin with an introductory paragraph about your topic. Then develop your topic in body paragraphs with facts, definitions, and details. Finally, write an interesting conclusion to your article.

Responses will vary but drafts should include an introduction; body paragraphs with facts, details, and definitions; and a conclusion.

Produce Sentences Using Adjectives

DIRECTIONS Write three sentences that include at least one adjective. Circle the adjective(s) in each sentence.

Rocks become (tiny) grains of sand after (many) years.

I hiked up the (highest) mountain in the state.

Leila is (taller) than her brother.

Students write routinely for a range of tasks, purposes, and audiences. Students practice various conventions of standard English.

Name ______________________________

Benchmark Vocabulary

DIRECTIONS Write a sentence using each word.

thunderstorm lightning electricity

Responses should show contextual understanding of the word.

Write in Response to Reading

Reread pp. 22–23. Why do you think thunderstorms happen more frequently during the spring and summer?

Responses should use evidence from the text, including that thunderstorms happen when there is warm air near the ground. This is most likely to be in spring and summer.

Students demonstrate contextual understanding of Benchmark Vocabulary. Students read text closely and use text evidence in their written answers.

Name ______________________________

Explain Scientific Ideas and Concepts

DIRECTIONS Using evidence from the text, answer the following questions about pp. 22–25 from *About Earth.*

1. What always occurs along with thunder during a storm?

lightning

2. What causes lightning?

Lightning is caused by bits of ice bumping against one another in a storm cloud.

3. What contributes to the formation of both wind and thunderstorms?

Rising warm air contributes to the formation of wind and thunderstorms.

4. Where do the coolest winds begin?

They begin over the sea.

Students analyze and respond to literary and informational text.

Writing

Name ______________________________

Revise On a separate sheet of paper, revise the article you drafted in Lesson 13. Make sure your topic is clear and your article includes facts and details that support your main idea.

Responses will vary but revisions should include a clear topic and ideas supported by relevant facts and details.

Conventions

Coordinating Conjunctions

DIRECTIONS Underline the coordinating conjunction in each sentence, and identify whether it connects two words, two phrases, or two sentences.

1. Lois will not go with us to the play, but she will join us for dinner.
   two sentences

2. Frances told Juan he could have candy or soda as a treat.
   two words

3. I always avoid going to the grocery store and driving on the highway during the holidays.
   two phrases

Students write routinely for a range of tasks, purposes, and audiences. Students practice various conventions of standard English.

Benchmark Vocabulary

Name ______________________________

DIRECTIONS Write a sentence using each word.

earthquake volcano oozing plates magma

Responses should show contextual understanding of the word.

Write in Response to Reading

How are earthquakes and volcanoes similar? How are earthquakes and volcanoes different?

Responses should use evidence from the text, including that they are similar because both earthquakes and volcanoes happen when Earth's plates move. They are different because only volcanoes have magma that bursts up through the plates.

Students demonstrate contextual understanding of Benchmark Vocabulary. Students read text closely and use text evidence in their written answers.

Writing

Name ______________________________

Edit and Present On a separate sheet of paper, edit your article. Check the spelling, capitalization, punctuation, and grammar.

Responses will vary but should include edits to spelling, capitalization, and punctuation errors.

Conventions

Coordinating Conjunctions

DIRECTIONS Circle the coordinating conjunction in each sentence. Identify whether the conjunction creates a compound subject, verb, or direct object.

1. Volcanoes erupt (and) spew magma. **compound verb**
2. You can take a toy (and) a book with you. **compound direct object**
3. Lyle (or) Fran will pick him up from the airport. **compound subject**

Students write routinely for a range of tasks, purposes, and audiences. Students practice various conventions of standard English.

Name ______________________________

Final Syllable *-le*

DIRECTIONS On the lines, write the two syllables that make up each word.

1. gig + gle = giggle
2. rid + dle = riddle
3. cy + cle = cycle
4. whee + dle = wheedle
5. war + ble = warble
6. ta + ble = table
7. mum + ble = mumble
8. sad + dle = saddle
9. tin + gle = tingle
10. tur + tle = turtle

DIRECTIONS Use words from the Word Bank to complete the sentences. You will not use all of the words.

Word Bank

noodle	poodle	people	uncle	juggle	trouble

11. My uncle was waving his arms around.
12. He was trying to juggle the spaghetti on his fork.
13. Every time he got a noodle, he lost it again.
14. That's because our big, smart poodle grabbed it!
15. Who knew eating pasta could be such trouble?

Students apply grade-level phonics and word analysis skills.

Benchmark Vocabulary

Name ______________________________

DIRECTIONS Write a sentence using each word.

contain liquid oozing survive

Responses should show contextual understanding of the word.

Write in Response to Reading

How do the definitions in the glossary on p. 32 help you better understand ideas in the text? Use specific examples from the text in your answer.

Responses will vary but should include that understanding the meaning of the words will help clarify the meaning of the ideas.

Students demonstrate contextual understanding of Benchmark Vocabulary. Students read text closely and use text evidence in their written answers.

Writing

Name ____________________

Publish and Present Write down notes and ideas for presenting your article to the class. Practice presenting your article as though you are a reporter delivering a news story, including illustrations and other text features. Then present your article to the class.

Responses will vary but should include notes and ideas for presenting the student's article to the class.

Conventions

Coordinating Conjunctions

DIRECTIONS Circle the coordinating conjunction in each sentence, and underline the two phrases that it connects.

1. Christine always arrives on time but never buys her ticket in advance.
2. Keep your phone in your pocket or in your bag.
3. Emma likes reading books and listening to music.

Students write routinely for a range of tasks, purposes, and audiences. Students practice various conventions of standard English.

Name ______________________________

Benchmark Vocabulary

DIRECTIONS Write a sentence using each word.

phases fascinated planet

Responses should show contextual understanding of the word.

Write in Response to Reading

Review the text features the authors use in *The Moon Seems to Change, Treasure in the Trees,* and *About Earth.* Identify the most useful text feature in each text, and explain how it helped you understand a key idea or message.

Responses will vary but should include how each text feature illustrated a key idea or message of the text.

Students demonstrate contextual understanding of Benchmark Vocabulary. Students read text closely and use text evidence in their written answers.

Name ______________________________

Text Features

DIRECTIONS Using evidence from the texts, answer the following questions about *The Moon Seems to Change, Treasure in the Trees,* and *About Earth.*

1. Look at the illustration on p. 3 of *About Earth.* Now look at the top illustration on p. 45 of *The Moon Seems to Change.* Both show Earth and the sun. How are these illustrations different? Why are they different?

   About Earth **shows other planets but no moon.** ***The Moon Seems to Change*** **shows the moon but no planets except Earth. The pictures leave out information unrelated to the main ideas to make the illustrations easier to understand.**

2. How do the headings in *About Earth* and *Treasure in the Trees* help you understand the texts?

   Responses may vary but could include that the headings in ***About Earth*** **help separate information and the headings (chapter titles) in** ***Treasure in the Trees*** **help emphasize important parts of the plot.**

3. Which text feature can you find in all three texts?

   All three texts have illustrations.

Students analyze and respond to literary and informational text.

Name ______________________

Writing

Take Notes and Sort Evidence Choose a topic and research it. Gather evidence from that research, and in the space below or on a separate sheet of paper, sort the evidence into categories. Use a graphic organizer to help you sort the evidence, if necessary.

Responses will vary but should include sorted evidence about the topic the student has chosen.

Conventions

Use Coordinating Conjunctions

DIRECTIONS Complete each sentence with the correct coordinating conjunction.

1. Fred is friendly **and** funny, so everyone likes him.
2. The bus is either early **or** late, but it's never on time.
3. We can study for the test here **or** at the library, but we have to make a decision soon.

Students write routinely for a range of tasks, purposes, and audiences. Students practice various conventions of standard English.

Benchmark Vocabulary

Name ______________________________

DIRECTIONS Write a sentence using the word.

observation

Responses should show contextual understanding of the word.

Write in Response to Reading

Identify one detail from *The Moon Seems to Change, Treasure in the Trees,* and *About Earth* that was key in helping you understand a main idea or central message in the text. Explain how it helped you understand that idea or message.

Responses should use evidence from the text.

Students demonstrate contextual understanding of Benchmark Vocabulary. Students read text closely and use text evidence in their written answers.

Name ________________________________

Gather Information to Build Knowledge Observe something in nature, using the texts you have read as models. On another sheet of paper, record your observations by making sketches and by writing and answering two or three questions that make your observations more accurate and detailed.

Responses will vary but should include sketches and observations, including those made in response to the student's questions.

Use Coordinating Conjunctions

DIRECTIONS Write three compound sentences that include coordinating conjunctions.

Linda can go to the store, or she can stay at home with me.

Sean had enough time to visit his friends, but he was not able to see everyone.

We stood beneath the shelter, and the snow piled up in front of us.

Students write routinely for a range of tasks, purposes, and audiences. Students practice various conventions of standard English.

Name ____________________

Compound Words

DIRECTIONS Identify the two words that make up each compound word. Write the words.

1. sun + glasses = sunglasses
2. rail + road = railroad
3. hair + cut = haircut
4. fire + house = firehouse
5. pop + corn = popcorn
6. my + self = myself
7. green + house = greenhouse
8. back + yard = backyard
9. rain + water = rainwater
10. sun + flower = sunflower

DIRECTIONS Choose the compound word to complete each sentence. Write the word on the line. Draw a line between the two words that make up each compound word.

grandfather **11.** My (grandfather/uncle) lives on a farm.

whenever **12.** I help him (whenever/when) I visit.

snowstorm **13.** Last winter, there was a terrible (blizzard/snowstorm).

outside **14.** We had to work (quickly/outside) in the cold.

sometimes **15.** It's (sometimes/often) difficult to be a farmer.

Students apply grade-level phonics and word analysis skills.

Benchmark Vocabulary

Name ______________________________

DIRECTIONS Write a sentence using each word.

pioneers migrated preserve plentiful scarce

Responses should show contextual understanding of the word.

Write in Response to Reading

Read the final paragraph on page 76. Do you think the Athabascans succeeded at "learning the new ways of a new world," while still practicing the old ways? Use details from the text to support your opinion.

Responses may vary but should include that the Athabascans were successful in the new ways because they attended school.

Students demonstrate contextual understanding of Benchmark Vocabulary. Students read text closely and use text evidence in their written answers.

Writing

Name ______________________________

Research and Gather Information Use "Finding Food" and "Camping" in the text and your own knowledge to come up with details that could be used in a story. First, record details about old and new ways of finding food and setting up camp using the text and your own knowledge. Then, write a few sentences to explain how these details could be used in a story.

Responses will vary but should include old and new ways of finding food and setting up camp and a few sentences that explain how they could be used in a story.

Conventions

Start Sentences with Capital Letters

DIRECTIONS Rewrite the sentences below and capitalize the appropriate words.

we all had to chip in to buy the toy boat. it was very expensive, so we saved our money for three months. after we had saved enough money, we went to the store and bought it.

We all had to chip in to buy the toy boat. It was very expensive, so we saved our money for three months. After we had saved enough money, we went to the store and bought it.

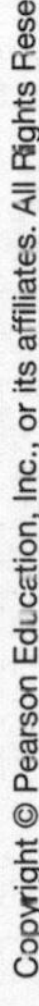

Students write routinely for a range of tasks, purposes, and audiences. Students practice various conventions of standard English.

Benchmark Vocabulary

Name ______________________________

DIRECTIONS Write a sentence using each word.

pioneers migrated scarce

Responses should show contextual understanding of the word.

Write in Response to Reading

Read page 65 and explain why the Athabascans chose to live like their ancestors did. Be sure to use evidence from the text.

Responses should use evidence from the text, including that "They wanted to learn and practice the skills passed down to them from their ancient Alaskan ancestors."

Students demonstrate contextual understanding of Benchmark Vocabulary. Students read text closely and use text evidence in their written answers.

Name ______________________________

Words Used for Effect

DIRECTIONS Using evidence from the text, answer the following questions about *The Athabascans: Old Ways and New Ways.*

1. Read the second paragraph on page 65. Find the word *pioneer.* Why did the author choose the word *pioneer?*

   The word *pioneer* helps the reader imagine and think about how pioneers lived and survived so that they can compare it to how the Athabascans lived.

2. Revisit the section "Camping." Read the sentence "We all had to chip in to make sure everyone was fed." What does "chip in" mean? Which details from the text help readers understand its meaning?

   They all had to work together. The text explains how each person contributed.

3. In the first paragraph in the section "One-Room Schoolhouses," read the sentence that begins, "He would have to watch out . . ." What effect do the words *big* and *hungry* have on the reader? What is the author's purpose for including them?

   The words *big* and *hungry* help the reader form a mental image of the bears while they read. The author wants readers to know that the man was scared of the bears.

4. In the section "One-Room Schoolhouses," read the sentence beginning, "Green, fiery, wolf orbs . . ." What effect do these words have on the reader?

   The descriptive words help the reader form a mental image of what the students and teacher saw as they walked home after school in the dark.

Students analyze and respond to literary and informational text.

Name ______________________

Writing

Write Notes for a Story Read "Getting Around" and "One-Room Schoolhouses" in the text, and take notes on details that interest you. Write a few sentences that explain how these details could be used in a story, as well as story ideas you came up with as you took notes.

Responses will vary but should include sentences that explain how details from "Getting Around" and "One-Room Schoolhouses" could be used in a story and story ideas that the student came up with as he or she took notes.

Conventions

Capitalize Appropriate Words in Titles

DIRECTIONS Rewrite each title and capitalize the appropriate words.

1. city homes **City Homes**
2. the year of miss agnes **The Year of Miss Agnes**
3. the song of sky and sand **The Song of Sky and Sand**

Students write routinely for a range of tasks, purposes, and audiences. Students practice various conventions of standard English.

Benchmark Vocabulary

Name ______________________________

DIRECTIONS Write a sentence using the word.

mileage

Responses should show contextual understanding of the word.

Write in Response to Reading

Read the dialogue about speaking English on pages 9–10. Based on the conversation about English, do you think the new teacher is a good teacher? Why or why not? Support your opinion with text evidence.

Responses should use evidence from the text.

Students demonstrate contextual understanding of Benchmark Vocabulary. Students read text closely and use text evidence in their written answers.

Name ______________________

Sleuth Work

A Visit to Vietnam

Benjamin's family left Vietnam when he was just a baby. Benjamin's dad had gotten a better job in Seattle, Washington. Every couple of years, his family went back to Vietnam to visit. This summer they were going for their longest visit yet—all summer!

After a long flight, their plane finally landed in Ho Chi Minh City. Benjamin couldn't wait to get to his grandparents' house. After his family picked up their luggage, they took a taxi through the busy streets. Benjamin had forgotten how many motorcycles and scooters zipped around the city.

The cab drove them past markets and street vendors. Benjamin licked his lips. He loved the fresh fruit and other delicious food in Vietnam.

Benjamin also loved looking at the different kinds of buildings. In one block, there were buildings that were hundreds of years old. Then, just a few blocks away, there were new shopping centers. Some of the stores and restaurants were the same ones Benjamin's family went to in Seattle.

Benjamin couldn't wait to see his grandparents. He loved pho, the special noodle soup his grandmother made. He liked sitting in the shady courtyard with his grandfather, who told stories about growing up in Vietnam.

His grandparents had also promised to take him to the beach this summer. Benjamin couldn't wait to go swimming in the South China Sea! There was so much he wanted to see and do. This was going to be the best summer ever!

Students read text closely to determine what the text says.

Sleuth Work

Name ______________________________

Gather Evidence How does Benjamin feel about his trip to Vietnam? Circle 5 words and phrases from the story that support your answer.

See annotations on previous page. Sample response: Benjamin was excited to go back to Vietnam. He was excited to see his grandparents and their house, eat pho, go swimming in the South China Sea, and much more.

Ask Questions Write 2–3 questions you have about Vietnam that can be answered from the text.

Responses will vary but could include: Is Seattle different from Ho Chi Minh City? Will Benjamin like the food in Vietnam?

Make Your Case What do you think is the main idea that the writer wants to share? Underline 2–3 key details that support the main idea.

Sample response: The main idea is that visiting a place far away can be exciting and interesting.

See annotations on previous page.

Students read text closely to determine what the text says.

Name ______________________

Writing

Genre Describe a story you would like to write. Then explain what genre it would be and why.

Responses will vary but should include the student's ideas for a story and an explanation of what genre the story would be.

Conventions

Capitalize Proper Nouns

DIRECTIONS Rewrite each sentence and capitalize the proper nouns.

1. Her sister laura goes to washington high school. **Her sister Laura goes to Washington High School.**

2. I visited aunt meg in dallas last november. **I visited Aunt Meg in Dallas last November.**

3. Maria is from spain, but she lives in brazil now. **Maria is from Spain, but she lives in Brazil now.**

Students write routinely for a range of tasks, purposes, and audiences. Students practice various conventions of standard English.

Benchmark Vocabulary

Name ______________________

DIRECTIONS Write a sentence using the word.

nuisance

Responses should show contextual understanding of the word.

Write in Response to Reading

Read the description of making clothes on pages 20–24. Write a paragraph that explains the process of making mittens, boots, or snowshoes. Write each step in the sequence, including the tasks done by Grandpa, Mamma, Grandma, and the sisters, Fred and Bokko. Support your explanation with evidence from the text.

Responses should use evidence from the text but should include that Grandpa traps the animals and gives the skins to Mamma, who scrapes the skins with a special knife until they're soft. Then she washes and hangs them to dry. While the skins are drying, she keeps twisting them so they don't dry stiff. Fred and Bokko help with this part. For the mittens, Mamma makes braided harnesses with pom-poms. Fred and Bokko help Mamma wrap the yarn around cardboard. Mamma makes boots from caribou legs, with an insole of caribou fur. She sews a band at the top that she makes with beads. Grandma makes sinew thread from the big hump of the moose and tans the moose hides with rotten moose brains.

Students demonstrate contextual understanding of Benchmark Vocabulary. Students read text closely and use text evidence in their written answers.

Name ____________________

Reading Analysis

Character

DIRECTIONS Using evidence from the text, answer the following questions about pages 14–15 of *The Year of Miss Agnes*.

1. How does Mamma feel about Fred going to school? What evidence from the text supports your answer?

Mamma is unhappy about Fred going to school. Fred describes her as "mad" and says that she was "slamming things around."

2. How does Fred feel about going to school? What evidence from the text supports your answer?

Fred is excited about going to school. She says that she is "so happy to be going to school again" and "glad to be going to school." She gets ready for school even though Mamma does not want her to go, and she runs all the way to school.

3. How does Bokko feel about Fred going to school? What evidence from the text supports your answer?

Bokko is happy that Fred is going to school. She helps Fred get ready and gives her clean socks to wear.

4. What is Fred able to do that Mamma cannot do? What does this reveal about her character?

Unlike Mamma, she can understand what Bokko wants to say. This shows that Fred is caring.

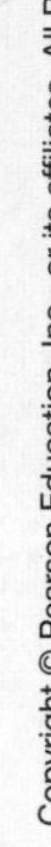

Students analyze and respond to literary and informational text.

Name ______________________________

Establish a Situation Write an opening paragraph that introduces the main character, describes the setting, and establishes the situation for your story.

Responses will vary but should include a paragraph that describes the main character, setting, and situation in the student's story.

Use Adverbs

DIRECTIONS Complete each sentence with an adverb.

1. Nora walked **quickly** to her seat.
2. Marion read the book **quietly**.
3. Jesse is **very** sick.

Students write routinely for a range of tasks, purposes, and audiences. Students practice various conventions of standard English.

Benchmark Vocabulary

Name ____________________

DIRECTIONS Write a sentence using each word.

cache margin freight

Responses should show contextual understanding of the word.

Write in Response to Reading

Read the last two paragraphs on pages 37–38. Was it a good idea for Miss Agnes to be "so picky" about her students' writing? Support your opinion with evidence from the text.

Responses should use evidence from the text.

Students demonstrate contextual understanding of Benchmark Vocabulary. Students read text closely and use text evidence in their written answers.

Name ______________________________

Introduce a Narrator and Characters Write a character sketch for a character that would appear in your narrative. Describe the character's physical traits, actions, motivations, and feelings.

Responses will vary but should include a description of a character's physical traits, actions, motivations, and feelings.

Function of Adverbs in a Sentence

DIRECTIONS Write a sentence with an adverb that performs the function identified, and underline the adverb.

1. Shows Location: **Shannon played basketball outside.**
2. Shows Time: **Nina's flight will arrive soon.**
3. Shows Frequency: **Loretta never drinks soda.**

Students write routinely for a range of tasks, purposes, and audiences. Students practice various conventions of standard English.

Name ______________________________

Consonant Blends (2- and 3-Letter)

DIRECTIONS Read the story. Underline the words with **2-letter consonant blends** (for example, *fl, pr,* and *st*). Then write the underlined words on the lines.

Ella stuffed her feet into her boots and trudged outdoors. As she drew close to the school, she saw her friends filling balloons. They filled them so full that they broke! Then one balloon flew up into the sky. Ella laughed. The girls began releasing full balloons, laughing as they watched them fly toward the clouds.

1. stuffed
2. trudged
3. drew
4. close
5. friends
6. broke
7. flew
8. sky
9. fly
10. clouds

DIRECTIONS Read each word out loud and listen for a **3-letter blend,** such as ***squ, spl, thr,*** or ***str.*** Then write two more words that start with the same blend. Underline the three-letter blend in each word you write.

11. straw str (e.g., street, stream, stroke)
12. splurge spl (e.g., splash, splinter, split)
13. squeak squ (e.g., square, squish, squat)
14. thread thr (e.g., three, thrum, throw)
15. strike str (e.g., string, strap, stretch)

Students apply grade-level phonics and word analysis skills.

Benchmark Vocabulary

Name ______________________________

DIRECTIONS Write a sentence using each word.

continents trader

Responses should show contextual understanding of the word.

Write in Response to Reading

Read the final paragraph of page 46. Write a paragraph explaining why the children would not get tired of having Miss Agnes for a teacher. Support your answer with text evidence.

Responses may vary and should show evidence from the text, such as that Miss Agnes taught them math so "no one could cheat us" and that Fred "didn't want school to end."

Students demonstrate contextual understanding of Benchmark Vocabulary. Students read text closely and use text evidence in their written answers.

Writing

Name ______________________________

Organize an Event Sequence Write a paragraph that describes an event sequence in which one event affects or causes another. Organize the events so that they unfold naturally.

Responses will vary but should include a sequence of events in which one event affects or causes another.

Conventions

Form Superlative Adverbs

DIRECTIONS Complete each sentence with a superlative adverb.

1. Myra ate her dinner **most quickly**.
2. Lou Ann works **best** early in the morning.
3. My dog Charlie runs the **fastest**.

Students write routinely for a range of tasks, purposes, and audiences. Students practice various conventions of standard English.

Benchmark Vocabulary

Name ______________________________

DIRECTIONS Write a sentence using the word.

deaf

Responses should show contextual understanding of the word.

Write in Response to Reading

Read the first full paragraph on page 53, which begins, "When Mamma stamped . . ." Write an opinion on whether Grandpa should have defended Mamma when she stomped out the door. Support your opinion with text evidence.

Responses should use evidence from the text.

Students demonstrate contextual understanding of Benchmark Vocabulary. Students read text closely and use text evidence in their written answers.

Name ___________________________

Character

DIRECTIONS Using evidence from the text, answer the following questions about Chapter 8 from *The Year of Miss Agnes.*

1. What does Bokko's trip to the school to bring Fred her lunch reveal about Bokko's character?

   Responses will vary but could include that the event reveals that Bokko is very caring.

2. How does Bokko's trip to the school to bring Fred's lunch affect Miss Agnes's actions?

   Responses will vary but could include that it leads to Miss Agnes deciding to teach Bokko.

3. What does Miss Agnes's conversation with Mamma reveal about Miss Agnes's character?

   Responses will vary but could include that it reveals that she is determined and persuasive.

4. What conflict does the conversation between Mamma and Miss Agnes lead to? Explain how the two events are related.

   It leads to an argument between Mamma and Grandpa about letting Bokko attend school.

5. What does this event reveal about Mamma's character?

   Responses will vary but could include that this event reveals that Mamma is very stubborn.

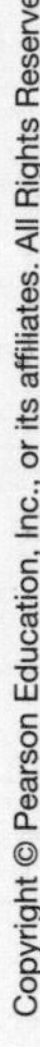

Students analyze and respond to literary and informational text.

Name ____________________

Writing

Use Temporal Words and Phrases to Signal Event Order Write a paragraph that uses temporal words and phrases to signal the order of events in an event sequence. Use the event sequence from Lesson 6 or create a new event sequence.

Responses will vary but should include temporal words and phrases that signal the order of events in an event sequence.

Conventions

Use Adverbs in a Sentence

DIRECTIONS Write a sentence with each adverb below.

1. slowly **Irene walked slowly to the principal's office.**

2. very **The principal was very patient with her.**

3. too **Irene was too upset to respond to his questions.**

Students write routinely for a range of tasks, purposes, and audiences. Students practice various conventions of standard English.

Benchmark Vocabulary

Name ______________________________

DIRECTIONS Write a sentence using the word.

catalog

Responses should show contextual understanding of the word.

Write in Response to Reading

Read page 67. Write a paragraph about what you think would be a better way to ask someone to dance. Support your opinion with text evidence.

Responses should use evidence from the text.

Students demonstrate contextual understanding of Benchmark Vocabulary. Students read text closely and use text evidence in their written answers.

Name ____________________

Writing

Use Dialogue to Develop Experiences Write a skit that tells more about an event that was mentioned only briefly in *The Year of Miss Agnes.* Use dialogue to develop the characters' experiences.

Responses will vary but should include a skit that tells more about an event mentioned briefly in *The Year of Miss Agnes* and uses dialogue to develop the characters' experiences.

Conventions

Review Commas in Dialogue

DIRECTIONS Write three sentences of dialogue. Place commas in the appropriate places.

Sample response: "I will go to the store for you, Mom," said Joe. "Thank you, Joe, you are a good son," replied Mom. "I'm always happy to help out," Joe answered, smiling at Mom.

Students write routinely for a range of tasks, purposes, and audiences. Students practice various conventions of standard English.

Benchmark Vocabulary

Name ______________________________

DIRECTIONS Write a sentence using each word.

snares goggled bluff

Responses should show contextual understanding of the word.

Write in Response to Reading

Read page 76, starting with the paragraph that begins, "Miss Agnes told him . . ." Was Miss Agnes right to appear angry with the students? State your opinion and support it with text evidence.

Responses should use evidence from the text.

Students demonstrate contextual understanding of Benchmark Vocabulary. Students read text closely and use text evidence in their written answers.

Name ________________________________

Use Dialogue to Show Character Responses Write dialogue that shows characters' responses. Use the characters you created in previous lessons or think of new characters.

Responses will vary but should include dialogue that shows characters' responses.

Review Quotation Marks in Dialogue

DIRECTIONS Write three sentences of dialogue using quotation marks correctly.

Sample response: "Jan, let's play hopscotch today, okay?" asked Maria. "Sure, Maria, I love playing hopscotch," answered Jan. "Yes! Let's race to the playground," said Maria.

Students write routinely for a range of tasks, purposes, and audiences. Students practice various conventions of standard English.

Benchmark Vocabulary

Name ______________________________

DIRECTIONS Write a sentence using each word.

brittle wringer

Responses should show contextual understanding of the word.

Write in Response to Reading

Read pages 94–95. Choose one student in the story, and tell what Miss Agnes said that he or she was good at doing. Then tell how she knew what the student's talent was. Use text evidence to support your answer.

Responses may vary but should show evidence from the text, such as Miss Agnes said Fred was good at writing stories. Miss Agnes knew this was Fred's talent and said, "Fred notices everything about everyone . . . So she's good at writing stories."

Students demonstrate contextual understanding of Benchmark Vocabulary. Students read text closely and use text evidence in their written answers.

Name ______________________

Character

DIRECTIONS Using evidence from the text, answer the following questions about pages 92–95 from *The Year of Miss Agnes.*

1. How do the books Miss Agnes writes for each student encourage the students to read in two ways?

   The students are excited to read the books Miss Agnes writes about them *and* the books she writes about other students.

2. What else does Miss Agnes do to help the students improve their reading skills?

   Responses may vary but could include that Miss Agnes makes them write stories and creates personal dictionaries for each student.

3. What does the assignment from Miss Agnes help reveal about Fred's character?

   Responses may vary but could include that the writing assignment helps reveal that Fred is a good writer.

4. Why do you think Miss Agnes tells each student what he or she is good at?

   Responses will vary but could include that Miss Agnes tells the students what they are good at because she cares about them and wants them to feel good about themselves.

Students analyze and respond to literary and informational text.

Writing

Name ______________________________

Use Descriptions to Develop Experiences Create a character sketch of Miss Agnes that describes her and the impact she has on the community.

Responses will vary but should include a description of Miss Agnes and her impact on the community.

Conventions

Use an Exclamation Mark in Dialogue

DIRECTIONS Write a dialogue below. Use at least two exclamation marks to show characters' strong feelings.

Sample response: "I don't want to go!" yelled Peter. "But we have to go, and we have to go now!" Joe yelled back at Peter, "It is beginning to thunder, and we don't want to get stuck in the rain."

Students write routinely for a range of tasks, purposes, and audiences. Students practice various conventions of standard English.

Name ________________________________

Consonant Digraphs

DIRECTIONS Write **sh, th, ph, ch, tch,** or **ng** to complete each word. Write the whole word on the line to the left.

purchased **1.** Maria's family pur ch ased a house.

mother **2.** Her mo th er decided to paint it.

brushes **3.** She bought bru sh es and buckets.

clothes **4.** Back home, she put on old clo th es.

patched **5.** Then she pa tch ed nail holes in the walls.

going **6.** Maria was goi ng to help choose colors.

phoned **7.** She ph oned a friend to talk it over.

choices **8.** The two of them made some ch oices.

shades **9.** Maria wanted sh ades of blue.

chose **10.** Her brother ch ose red instead.

DIRECTIONS Read each definition. Then write **sh, th, wh, ph,** or **ng** to complete the word that matches.

11. An award that looks like a statue or cup tro ph y

12. A mammal that lives in the ocean wh ale

13. Playground equipment that gets pushed swi ng

14. A person who participates in sports a th lete

15. Something a person can shrug sh oulder

Students apply grade-level phonics and word analysis skills.

Benchmark Vocabulary

Name ______________________________

DIRECTIONS Write a sentence using the word.

bunks

Responses should show contextual understanding of the word.

Write in Response to Reading

Read page 102. Do you think "young brains" are better than "old brains"? Use text evidence to support your opinion.

Responses should use evidence from the text.

Students demonstrate contextual understanding of Benchmark Vocabulary. Students read text closely and use text evidence in their written answers.

Writing

Name ______________________

Use Descriptions to Show Responses Look at the dialogue you wrote in Lesson 9. Write a paragraph that uses descriptions instead of dialogue to show a character's response.

Responses will vary but should include a paragraph that uses descriptions instead of dialogue to describe one of the characters' responses from Lesson 9.

Conventions

Use a Question Mark in Dialogue

DIRECTIONS Read page 105 in *The Year of Miss Agnes.* Write two questions that students might ask Miss Agnes. Place a question mark in the appropriate place in each line of dialogue.

Sample responses: Why won't you come back to our school next year? What will you do when you leave this school?

Students write routinely for range of tasks, purposes, and audiences. Students practice various conventions of standard English.

Name ___________________________

Benchmark Vocabulary

DIRECTIONS Write a sentence using the word.

invented

Responses should show contextual understanding of the word.

Write in Response to Reading

Read the first complete paragraph on page 111. Explain why so many things reminded Fred and Bokko of Miss Agnes. Use text evidence to support your answer.

Responses may vary but should show evidence from the text, such as that Miss Agnes taught them math and now Fred and Bokko could count up all the fish caught weekly at fish camp and then add the numbers together.

Students demonstrate contextual understanding of Benchmark Vocabulary. Students read text closely and use text evidence in their written answers.

Name ______________________________

Character

DIRECTIONS Using evidence from the text, answer the following questions about pages 109–111 from *The Year of Miss Agnes.*

1. How have Bokko's feelings changed about being around other people?

   Bokko is no longer afraid and shy around other people.

2. How do Bokko's actions around her family change as a result?

   She teaches everyone sign language so that she can talk to them.

3. What are Fred and Bokko able to do during fish camp because they have been in school?

   They are able to add up the fish that they have caught during the week.

4. How does Mamma respond to Fred and Bokko using the skills they learned in school? How does Fred describe Mamma's feelings?

   Mamma acts as though she knew that Bokko and Fred could add and does not say anything, but Fred says that she knows Mamma is proud.

5. Why do you think Mamma's actions do not show her feelings?

   Responses may vary but could include that they are different because Mamma is still stubborn and does not like to show her feelings.

Students analyze and respond to literary and informational text.

Writing

Name ____________________

Provide a Sense of Closure Write an ending for your story that provides a sense of closure.

Responses will vary but should include an ending for the student's story that provides a sense of closure.

Conventions

Review Subject-Verb Agreement in Sentences

DIRECTIONS Write three sentences with correct subject-verb agreement. Include at least one sentence with a singular subject and one sentence with a plural subject.

Sample response: Jane loves writing stories. Max and Evan play clarinet in the band. He sleeps late on Saturday.

Students write routinely for a range of tasks, purposes, and audiences. Students practice various conventions of standard English.

Name ________________________________

DIRECTIONS Write a sentence using each word.

migrated   plentiful   cache   margin   brittle

Responses should show contextual understanding of the word.

Write in Response to Reading

How do *The Athabascans: Old Ways and New Ways* and *The Year of Miss Agnes* help you understand how people can learn to practice both old and new ways? Use text evidence to support your answer.

Responses will vary but should include text evidence about how both books talk about how native Alaskans followed the old ways (such as going to fish camp, which is noted in both books) while practicing new ways, including going to school.

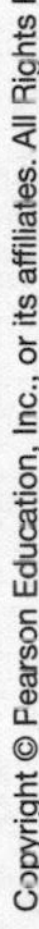

Students demonstrate contextual understanding of Benchmark Vocabulary. Students read text closely and use text evidence in their written answers.

Name ______________________________

A Day at School in Japan

Have you ever wondered how a school day in Japan might compare to one of yours?

Like many students in the United States, many Japanese elementary school students start their day around 8:30 a.m. and end around 3:00 p.m. They have math and reading classes. They listen to announcements at the start of the day. The teacher takes attendance. During the week, students might gather for an assembly where the principal or someone else talks to them.

There are a number of differences too. For example, in the United States, students learn handwriting. In Japan, students learn *shodo,* or calligraphy. This involves dipping a brush into ink and writing symbols. The symbols stand for words. Students in Japan also have a class where they learn how to cook and sew.

If you think school is hard in America, think about what students in Japan must do. They often have more homework than students in the United States do. They also spend at least six more weeks in school each year. Some schools also assign chores to students. Sweeping and cleaning the floor, wiping the board, and emptying the trash are some of these chores.

If you were an American student in a Japanese school, do you think it would be difficult to adjust to these differences? Remember, you would have to do everything in a completely different language, too.

Students read text closely to determine what the text says.

Sleuth Work

Name ______________________________

Gather Evidence How does a day at school in Japan compare to your school day in the United States?

Responses will vary but should include text evidence, such as that students in Japan learn *shodo* and how to cook and sew.

Ask Questions Write three questions you would ask a student from Japan about his or her day at school. Underline sentences or phrases from the text that answer your questions.

Responses will vary.

Make Your Case What is the most interesting dctail you can learn from the images that support the idea that schools in Japan are different from schools here? Can you find that detail in the text?

Responses will vary but could include that students use paintbrushes as well as pencils.

Students read text closely to determine what the text says.

Name ______________________________

Writing

Review the Elements of Narrative Writing Write a paragraph for a narrative, using one or more of the elements of narrative writing.

Responses will vary but should include a paragraph that uses one or more of the elements of narrative writing.

Conventions

Subject-Verb Agreement with Regular Verbs

DIRECTIONS Complete each sentence with the correct form of the verb in parentheses.

1. Laura and Felicia climbed (climb) the hill yesterday.
2. Sylvia marches (march) up the stairs to her room and starts her homework.
3. Wendy talks (talk) to her best friend as they walk to class.

Students write routinely for a range of tasks, purposes, and audiences. Students practice various conventions of standard English.

Benchmark Vocabulary

Name ______________________________

DIRECTIONS Write a sentence using each word.

suitor	threshold	mourned	consent	summons
morsel	feast	unnatural	exchange	

Responses should show contextual understanding of the word.

Write in Response to Reading

Read page 86 of *The Frog Princess.* Write a few sentences explaining how the girl felt when she was with the Frog People. How do her feelings about the Frog People shape the rest of the story? Support your answer with text evidence.

Responses should use evidence from the text, including that the girl was happy with the Frog People. She enjoyed her time with them so much that she forgot about time.

Students demonstrate contextual understanding of Benchmark Vocabulary. Students read text closely and use text evidence in their written answers.

Name ______________________

Writing

Plan and Prewrite a Narrative Gather information and take notes below on characters and events in legends to plan an extension of *The Frog Princess.* Then use the Story Sequence B graphic organizer to plan your narrative.

Responses will vary but should include notes on characters and events in legends.

Conventions

Subject-Verb Agreement with Irregular Verbs in Sentences

DIRECTIONS Use each irregular verb below in a sentence with the tense and subject identified.

1. *take* (present tense, singular subject) My brother takes my bag by accident.

2. *do* (past tense, plural subject) Noah and Maria did their homework quietly.

3. *go* (past tense, singular subject) She went to the beach last weekend.

Students write routinely for a range of tasks, purposes, and audiences. Students practice various conventions of standard English.

Benchmark Vocabulary

Name ______________________________

DIRECTIONS Write a sentence using each word.

consent   exchange   summons

Responses should show contextual understanding of the word.

Write in Response to Reading

Does the girl's attitude in *The Frog Princess* change as the story goes along? Support your opinion using text evidence.

Responses should use evidence from the text, including that at the beginning of the story no one is good enough for her, but after joining the Frog People, she is only happy there and with her frog husband.

Students demonstrate contextual understanding of Benchmark Vocabulary. Students read text closely and use text evidence in their written answers.

Name ___________________________

Determine the Central Message

DIRECTIONS Using evidence from the text, answer the following questions about *The Frog Princess.*

1. What key details from the story show the reader how the Frog Princess feels about being with the Frog People?

   Responses will vary but could include that "the girl enjoyed the feasting and dancing so much that she forgot about time" and that the frog chief says, "She is happy with us."

2. What key details from the story show the reader how the Frog Princess feels about being at home again?

   Responses will vary but could include that the girl "sat with her eyes lowered, looking very sad" and that the girl says, "I miss my husband and children."

3. What key details from the story show the reader how the Frog Princess feels about returning to live with the Frog People?

   Responses will vary but could include that a frog asks the traveler to tell the headman that "his daughter is well" and that "she is happy here with her husband and children."

4. What central message do these details help communicate?

   Responses will vary but should include something about a person finding a community in which they belong.

Students analyze and respond to literary and informational text.

Name ____________________

Draft a Narrative Draft your extension of *The Frog Princess.* Be sure to establish a situation with a problem or conflict, include a short, organized sequence of events, and resolve the situation.

Responses will vary but should include a draft of an extension of *The Frog Princess* that establishes a situation with a problem or conflict, includes a short, organized sequence of events, and resolves the situation.

Review Simple Sentences

DIRECTIONS Write three simple sentences. One sentence should have a plural subject.

Sample response: Jane loves french fries. Bob and Burt have the flu. Petra ran a race.

Students write routinely for a range of tasks, purposes, and audiences. Students practice various conventions of standard English.

Name ______________________________

Contractions

DIRECTIONS Use each pair of words to form a contraction. Write the contraction on the line.

haven't **1.** have not

when's **2.** when is

didn't **3.** did not

they'll **4.** they will

she's **5.** she is

you'll **6.** you will

we'd **7.** we would

I'd **8.** I would

let's **9.** let us

they're **10.** they are

that's **11.** that is

he'd **12.** he would

wasn't **13.** was not

you'd **14.** you had

DIRECTIONS Use the words in parentheses to make a contraction and complete each sentence. Write the contraction on the line.

hasn't **15.** Javier (has not) planted a garden before.

he'd **16.** This year he has decided (he would) like to try.

they'll **17.** His dad says (they will) work on it together.

wasn't **18.** Javier's sister told them it (was not) warm enough to begin.

it's **19.** She said seeds won't grow when (it is) too cold.

I've **20.** Javier said, "Gosh! (I have) never heard that before!"

Students apply grade-level phonics and word analysis skills.

Benchmark Vocabulary

Name ______________________________

DIRECTIONS Write a sentence using each word.

threshold morsel unnatural

Responses should show contextual understanding of the word.

Write in Response to Reading

Read pages 99–100 of *The Frog Princess.* Think about the actions of the girl, her family, and the shaman. Then write a few sentences describing the events on thosc pages. Be sure to describe the events in the same order that they happen in the text, and use text evidence in your description.

Responses should use evidence from the text, including that the headman brought his daughter home and found she could not speak. They prepared a feast for her, but she did not eat. The shaman prepared and gave her a healing mixture to drive out the bad spirits. She drank the potion and vomited a ball of mud. She awakened as if from a dream and spoke but was still sad. She missed her husband and children.

Students demonstrate contextual understanding of Benchmark Vocabulary. Students read text closely and use text evidence in their written answers.

Name ______________________

Writing

Revise a Narrative Revise your story. Emphasize the traits of your characters, and make sure that your event sequence flows naturally and ends with a logical resolution to the problem in the story.

Responses will vary but should include a revised narrative that emphasizes the characters' traits, has an event sequence that flows naturally, and ends with a logical resolution to the problem in the story.

Conventions

Define Compound Sentences

DIRECTIONS Underline the two independent clauses in each compound sentence, and circle the coordinating conjunction that connects them.

1. The woman spoke calmly to her grandchildren, (but) they did not pay attention to her.
2. My brother can go to Anderson Middle School, (or) he can be homeschooled.
3. Nina went to the park, (and) she played baseball with her friends.

Students write routinely for a range of tasks, purposes, and audiences. Students practice various conventions of standard English.

Benchmark Vocabulary

Name ______________________________

DIRECTIONS Write a sentence using each word.

freight continents mourned feast

Responses should show contextual understanding of the word.

Write in Response to Reading

The parents in both texts make decisions about their children's lives based on their own experiences. Should parents make these decisions for their children? Why or why not? Support your opinion with text evidence.

Responses should use evidence from the text.

Students demonstrate contextual understanding of Benchmark Vocabulary. Students read text closely and use text evidence in their written answers.

Name ____________________

Compare and Contrast

DIRECTIONS Using evidence from the texts, answer the following questions about *The Year of Miss Agnes* and *The Frog Princess.*

1. What is one way that the author develops the central message that people should accept new possibilities without ignoring old traditions in *The Year of Miss Agnes*?

   Responses will vary but could include that the author develops this idea through Mamma's change in attitude about Fred and Bokko going to school.

2. Is this idea developed in *The Frog Princess*? If so, what key details help develop this message?

   Responses will vary but could include the frog princess's family losing her again because they believe that humans and frogs should only live among their own kind.

3. What is one way that the author develops the central message that people should respect others' choices in *The Frog Princess*?

   The girl's decision to leave her family for good helps develop this message.

4. Is this idea developed in *The Year of Miss Agnes*? If so, what key details help develop this message?

   Responses will vary but could include Mamma allowing both Fred and Bokko to go to school even though she does not want them to go.

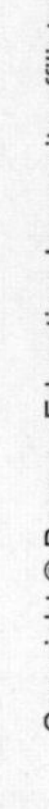

Students analyze and respond to literary and informational text.

Writing

Name ___________________________

Edit a Narrative Correct any errors in grammar, spelling, punctuation, and capitalization in your story. Then, using those corrections and feedback from a partner, write your final draft on a separate sheet of paper.

Responses will vary but should include an edited version of the student's story that uses correct grammar, spelling, punctuation, and capitalization.

Conventions

Produce Compound Sentences

DIRECTIONS Combine each pair of sentences using either a coordinating conjunction or a semicolon.

1. Norman wanted to buy the guitar. It was too expensive.

Answers will vary. Norman wanted to buy the guitar, but it was too expensive.

2. He did have enough money for a small drum. He bought one.

Answers will vary. He did have enough money for a small drum, so he bought one.

3. He liked playing the drum. It helped him express his emotions.

Answers will vary. He liked playing the drum; it helped him express his emotions.

Students write routinely for a range of tasks, purposes, and audiences. Students practice various conventions of standard English.

Benchmark Vocabulary

Name ______________________________

DIRECTIONS Write a sentence using each word.

pioneers preserve scarce nuisance snares goggled

Responses should show contextual understanding of the word.

Write in Response to Reading

Think about what the three texts tell you about the differences between old ways and new ways. Why do people want to live in old ways? Why do they want to try new ways? Support your opinion with text evidence.

Responses should use evidence from the text.

Students demonstrate contextual understanding of Benchmark Vocabulary. Students read text closely and use text evidence in their written answers.

Writing

Name ______________________

Publish and Present Present your work by acting out scenes from the story you wrote. Write the scenes you will act out below or on a separate sheet of paper.

Responses will vary but should include scenes from the student's story that he or she will present.

Conventions

Produce Compound Sentences

DIRECTIONS Write a compound sentence with each coordinating conjunction below.

1. and **Karen will arrive in an hour, and Chris will arrive in two hours.**

2. so **I did not have any eggs, so I used applesauce in the batter.**

3. but **Lauren can make cupcakes, but she does not know how to make frosting.**

Students write routinely for a range of tasks, purposes, and audiences. Students practice various conventions of standard English.

Name ______________________

Prefixes *un-, re-, mis-, dis-, non-*

DIRECTIONS Add the prefix ***un-, re-, mis-, dis-,*** or ***non-*** to each base word. Write the new word on the line.

1. un + load = unload

2. re + learn = relearn

3. mis + direct = misdirect

4. dis + like = dislike

5. non + sense = nonsense

DIRECTIONS Write the word from the Word Bank that best fits each definition.

Word Bank

nonstop	dishonest	misspell	rewrite	unknown

misspell **6.** to spell incorrectly

nonstop **7.** without stopping

unknown **8.** not known

rewrite **9.** to write again

dishonest **10.** not truthful

DIRECTIONS Add the prefix ***un-, re-, mis-,*** or ***dis-*** to the word in parentheses to complete each sentence. Write the new word on the line.

unable **11.** Last night I was (able) to see the stars.

disappeared **12.** They seem to have (appeared) in the cloudy sky.

misplaced **13.** Anyway, someone has (placed) our telescope.

recall **14.** When I asked who used it last, no one could (call).

unlikely **15.** Tonight is cloudy, so it is (likely) the stars will be out.

Students apply grade-level phonics and word analysis skills.

Benchmark Vocabulary

Name ______________________________

DIRECTIONS Write a sentence using each word.

townhouses suburbs apartments concrete streetcars

Responses should show contextual understanding of the word.

Write in Response to Reading

Think about the different types of homes described in *City Homes*. Which type of home would you want to live in? State your opinion and support it with text evidence.

Responses should use evidence from the text.

Students demonstrate contextual understanding of Benchmark Vocabulary. Students read text closely and use text evidence in their written answers.

Writing

Name ______________________

Conveying Ideas and Information Choose a topic and write an informative/explanatory paragraph about it. Your paragraph should express your views about the topic while providing factual information.

Responses will vary but should include an informative/ explanatory paragraph that expresses the student's views about a topic and provides factual information.

Conventions

Review the Definition of Adverbs

DIRECTIONS Circle the adverb(s) in each sentence, and underline the word that it modifies. Then identify whether the word it modifies is a verb, adjective, or adverb.

1. The soup is very hot. **adjective**
2. Margaret ate her lunch slowly. **verb**
3. Victor walked too quickly. **adverb, verb**

Students write routinely for a range of tasks, purposes, and audiences. Students practice various conventions of standard English.

Benchmark Vocabulary

Name ________________________________

DIRECTIONS Write a sentence using each word.

townhouses suburbs apartments

Responses should show contextual understanding of the word.

Write in Response to Reading

Read the "School and play" section of *City Homes*. Write an informative paragraph describing some of the things people can do for entertainment in a city.

Responses should use evidence from the text, including visiting parks and city zoos, going to theaters and cinemas to see plays and films, visiting libraries to read books, and going to swimming pools and places for playing sports.

Students demonstrate contextual understanding of Benchmark Vocabulary. Students read text closely and use text evidence in their written answers.

Name ________________________________

Literal and Nonliteral Meanings

DIRECTIONS Using evidence from the text, answer the following questions about page 113 of *City Homes.*

1. What is the meaning of the word *cold* as it is used on page 113? Is this a literal or nonliteral meaning of the word?

   The word *cold* means having a very low temperature on p. 113, and this a literal meaning of the word.

2. If the word *cold* has a literal meaning on page 113, what is a nonliteral meaning of the word? If the word *cold* has a nonliteral meaning on page 113, what is a literal meaning of the word?

   Responses may vary but could include that the nonliteral meaning of *cold* is showing no emotion or being unfriendly.

3. What is the meaning of the word *warm* as it is used on page 113? Is this a literal or nonliteral meaning of the word?

   The word *warm* means having a moderate temperature, or being neither hot nor cold, and this a literal meaning of the word.

4. If the word *warm* has a literal meaning on page 113, what is a nonliteral meaning of the word? If the word *warm* has a nonliteral meaning on page 113, what is a literal meaning of the word?

   Responses may vary but could include that the nonliteral meaning of *warm* is friendly.

Students analyze and respond to literary and informational text.

Name ______________________

Understanding Different Genres On a separate sheet of paper, complete a Web B graphic organizer to compare and contrast three genres of informative writing: procedural writing, report writing, and explanatory writing. Place "Informative Writing" in the center oval and "Procedural Writing," "Report Writing," and "Explanatory Writing" in the outer ovals. In each oval, write the features of that genre. Then write 2–4 sentences that explain how the three genres of writing are similar and different on the lines below.

Responses will vary but should include a completed graphic organizer and 2–4 sentences about the similarities and differences among procedural writing, report writing, and explanatory writing.

Review How Adverbs Function in a Sentence

DIRECTIONS Underline the adverb in each sentence. Then tell which word it modifies, the type of word it modifies, and what sort of information it adds to the sentence.

1. Traffic moves slowly during rush hour. ***Slowly* modifies the verb *moves* and tells how the traffic moves.**

2. We drove to Milwaukee yesterday. ***Yesterday* modifies the verb *drove* and tells when they drove.**

3. The engine in my car is very hot. ***Very* modifies the adjective *hot* and tells how hot the engine is.**

Students write routinely for a range of tasks, purposes, and audiences. Students practice various conventions of standard English.

Benchmark Vocabulary

Name ______________________________

DIRECTIONS Write a sentence using each word.

concrete streetcars

Responses should show contextual understanding of the word.

Write in Response to Reading

Read the section of *City Homes* titled "The weather." The author shows photographs of buildings in different climates. Are the photographs effective? State your opinion. Then use evidence from the text to support it.

Responses should use evidence from the text. Answer could be yes, the pictures are effective because they show wind catchers on buildings in a warm climate and a snowy scene in a cold climate. Answer could be no, although the pictures show a warm place and a cold place, they can't really give you the total feeling of temperature. You can only understand that if you add words to explain how cold it is, or if you are actually there.

Students demonstrate contextual understanding of Benchmark Vocabulary. Students read text closely and use text evidence in their written answers.

Name ______________________________________

A Visit to Cuba

"We're going to visit Grandma!" Manny exclaimed to his little brother Leon.

"I wonder if Cuba is anything like New York City." Leon said.

Traveling to Cuba took several hours. The boys were excited to finally spot the island of Cuba outside the airplane window. On the taxi ride to Grandma's house, they got a glimpse of the city of Old Havana. The city was busy just like New York City. The honking horns made the boys feel at home.

The next day Grandmother took them to see some of her favorite places. The market had vegetables that were unusual to the boys. They enjoyed eating lunch at a restaurant outside under some tall palm trees. Colorful birds sang loudly overhead. After lunch they toured the city to see some of its biggest buildings.

"New York City has much taller buildings," thought Leon.

They stopped to listen to a band playing local instruments. Manny danced to the beat of the bongo drums.

After a week of fun, the visit had come to an end. The boys stood at the door to say goodbye. Grandmother said, "I have some gifts for you. They will help you remember your trip to Cuba." Leon unwrapped a special whistle that made sounds just like the songs the birds had sung at the restaurant. Manny opened a box with a set of bongo drums. "Now New York City can sound a little more like Cuba," laughed Grandmother.

Students read text closely to determine what the text says.

Name ______________________________

Gather Evidence Underline the details in the story that help you to learn about life in Old Havana. **Responses will vary.**

Gather Evidence: Extend Your Ideas Work with a partner, and discuss how important these details are to the story. Write 2–3 sentences explaining how important they are.

Responses should use evidence from the text.

____

____

Ask Questions What questions would you ask the boys about the trip to Cuba? Are they discussed in the text? If so, circle that section of the text.

Responses will vary.

____

Ask Questions: Extend Your Ideas What question would you ask the boys about the trip to Cuba that is not answered in the text? Research your question and write 1–2 sentences discussing it.

Responses will vary.

____

Make Your Case Do you think Old Havana and New York City have more similarities or differences? Underline key words or phrases that help answer the question. **Responses will vary.**

Make Your Case: Extend Your Ideas Research New York City and Old Havana. Using the information you find, write 2–3 sentences about how they are similar and different. Discuss your results with a partner.

Responses will vary.

____

____

Students read text closely to determine what the text says.

Name ______________________________

Write a Description of Graphics Describe and analyze a photograph, using evidence from the text and the photograph to show how geography influences a way of life. Write a few sentences that describe the details in the photograph and a few sentences that explain what these details tell about how geography influences life.

Responses will vary but should include several sentences that describe the details in a photograph and explain what those details tell about how geography influences life.

Review Using Adverbs in a Sentence

DIRECTIONS Write a sentence using each adverb below.

1. politely **She asked politely for another slice of pizza.**

2. never **His mother never rides the train.**

3. quite **Our dog is quite friendly.**

Students write routinely for a range of tasks, purposes, and audiences. Students practice various conventions of standard English.

Benchmark Vocabulary

Name ______________________________

DIRECTIONS Write a sentence using each word.

similar characters extreme

Responses should show contextual understanding of the word.

Write in Response to Reading

Describe the similarities between the places where most people live. Why do you think most people live in places with those characteristics? Use text evidence in your response.

Responses should use evidence from the text, including that most people live where it is not too hot or cold, in or near cities, and within 100 miles of the sea. Student opinions may vary.

Students demonstrate contextual understanding of Benchmark Vocabulary. Students read text closely and use text evidence in their written answers.

Name ____________________

Main Idea

DIRECTIONS Using evidence from the text, answer the following questions about pages 4–5 from *Deep Down and Other Extreme Places to Live.*

1. How much of the world's population lives in or near a city?

More than half of the people in the world live in or near a city.

2. What main idea does this detail help develop?

This detail helps develop the idea that most people live in similar places.

3. Which types of places cover a lot of Earth?

Jungles, mountains, deserts, and large areas of snow cover a lot of Earth.

4. What main idea does this detail help develop?

This detail helps develop the idea that some people live in extreme places.

5. Why might these places be "extreme" places to live?

Responses will vary but could include that they might be extreme because they are very hot or very cold.

Students analyze and respond to literary and informational text.

Writing

Name ______________________

Introduce a Topic Write an introduction to a topic that appears in *Deep Down and Other Extreme Places to Live,* such as deserts.

Responses will vary but should include an introduction to a topic from *Deep Down and Other Extreme Places to Live.*

Conventions

Review Using Coordinating Conjunctions in a Sentence

DIRECTIONS Use each coordinating conjunction below in a sentence. Then explain how it links ideas, contrasts ideas, or offers a choice.

1. or William can buy a hot dog or a slice of piece. *Or* joins "a hot dog" and "a slice of pizza" and shows that William can choose between buying a hot dog and buying a slice of pizza.
2. but Laura is short, but Mary is tall. *But* joins "Laura is short" and "Mary is tall" and shows a contrast between the girls' heights.
3. and Tasha and Myron always finish their classwork early. The conjunction *and* connects *Tasha* and *Myron* and shows that they both finish their work early.

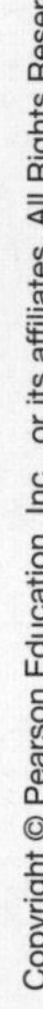

Students write routinely for a range of tasks, purposes, and audiences. Students practice various conventions of standard English.

Benchmark Vocabulary

Name ______________________________

DIRECTIONS Write a sentence using each word.

canyon emerald survive

Responses should show contextual understanding of the word.

____

____

____

____

Write in Response to Reading

On page 6 the author uses the word *spectacular* to describe the waterfalls near Supai. Look at the image of Havasu Falls on page 11. How would you describe the falls? How does this photograph help you understand the meaning of *spectacular*?

Responses will vary but could include that the falls are big, beautiful, and blue-green in color. The photo helps me understand the word "spectacular" because it shows how impressive and unforgettable the falls are.

____

____

Students demonstrate contextual understanding of Benchmark Vocabulary. Students read text closely and use text evidence in their written answers.

Writing

Name ______________________________

Develop a Topic Develop the topic you introduced in Lesson 4 by adding one or more paragraphs with facts, definitions, and details. Use the lines below or a separate sheet of paper.

Responses will vary but should include one or more paragraphs with facts, definitions, and details that develop the topic introduced in Lesson 4.

Conventions

Define Subordinating Conjunctions

DIRECTIONS Underline the subordinate clause in each sentence. Then circle the subordinating conjunction.

1. When I finish my lunch, I will go outside and play with my friends.
2. Bruce is sad because he lost his favorite toy.
3. Lisa's parents will pick her up after they leave the movie theater.

Students write routinely for a range of tasks, purposes, and audiences. Students practice various conventions of standard English.

Name ______________________

Spellings of /j/, /s/, and /k/

DIRECTIONS Underline the letter or letters that stand for the **/j/ sound** as in *jar*. Then write a sentence using each word.

1. gentle **Sample response: He was gentle with the kitten.**
2. bridge **Sample response: The bridge spanned the river.**
3. banjo **Sample response: His fingers flew when he played the banjo.**
4. village **Sample response: The village was far outside of town.**

DIRECTIONS Circle the words in the Word Bank that have the **/k/ sound** spelled *k, c, ck,* and *ch.* Write the words on the lines.

Word Bank

brake	branch	cellar	salad	merchant
peaceful	anchor	dresser	pluck	concrete

5. **brake**
6. **anchor**
7. **pluck**
8. **concrete**

DIRECTIONS Circle the words in the Word Bank that have the **/s/ sound** as in *person* or *pencil*. Write the words on the lines.

9. **cellar**
10. **salad**
11. **peaceful**
12. **dresser**

Students apply grade-level phonics and word analysis skills.

Name ______________________

Benchmark Vocabulary

DIRECTIONS Write a sentence using the word.

mine

Responses should show contextual understanding of the word.

Write in Response to Reading

Why is the Danakil Depression an extreme place to live? Use text evidence to support your answer.

Responses should use evidence from the text, including that it is one of the hottest places on Earth because it is heated by the sun above and lava flows below. Daily temperatures are more than 120°F. The winds are very hot and called fire winds, and it rains less than 7 inches a year.

Students demonstrate contextual understanding of Benchmark Vocabulary. Students read text closely and use text evidence in their written answers.

Name ______________________________

Use Illustrations to Aid Comprehension Find or draw illustrations for the topic you started writing about in Lesson 4, and then write captions for each one. If you find illustrations, attach them to this page, and write your captions below. If you draw illustrations, use a separate sheet of paper for your drawings and captions.

Responses will vary but should include illustrations with captions.

Use Subordinating Conjunctions in a Sentence

DIRECTIONS Combine each pair of sentences below using a subordinating conjunction.

1. We looked in the cupboard. Mom hides a bag of cookies there.

   Answers will vary. We looked in the cupboard because Mom hides a bag of cookies there.

2. Aunt Martha went to the store. She made dinner for us.

   Answers will vary. After Aunt Martha went to the store, she made dinner for us.

Students write routinely for a range of tasks, purposes, and audiences. Students practice various conventions of standard English.

Name ______________________

Benchmark Vocabulary

DIRECTIONS Write a sentence using each word.

evaporated provide herd

Responses should show contextual understanding of the word.

Write in Response to Reading

How do you think you would feel if you were one of the Afar people? Explain your answer using evidence from the text.

Responses will vary but should use text evidence to support opinions.

Students demonstrate contextual understanding of Benchmark Vocabulary. Students read text closely and use text evidence in their written answers.

Name ___________________________

Main Idea and Key Details

DIRECTIONS Using evidence from the text, answer the following questions about pages 14–17 from *Deep Down and Other Extreme Places to Live.*

1. Why is salt important to the Afar people?

It was once used as a form of money, but now they sell it as a source of income.

2. What sort of homes do the Afar people live in? How are these homes suited to their lifestyle?

The Afar people live in *aris*. These homes are suited to their nomadic lifestyle because they are portable.

3. Which two animals are especially important to the Afar people and why?

Camels and donkeys are important because the Afar people use them to mine salt, which they use as a source of income.

4. How do these details help develop a main idea?

Responses will vary but could include that these details show that the Afar have adapted well to their environment; they make a living using a natural resource and have used the resources available to them to make doing so easier.

Students analyze and respond to literary and informational text.

Name ____________________

Writing

Group Related Information Group related facts and key details about your topic. You can group this information by writing a paragraph below, creating lists on a separate sheet of paper, or completing a Main Idea organizer on a separate sheet of paper.

Responses will vary but should include a paragraph, lists, or a main idea organizer to group facts and key details about the student's topic.

Conventions

Review Plural Verbs

DIRECTIONS Rewrite each sentence using a plural subject, and change the verb to agree with the new subject.

1. She walks a long way to get home. **They walk a long way to get home.**

2. He listens to the radio at night. **He and his brother listen to the radio at night.**

3. It changes every month. **They change every month.**

Students write routinely for a range of tasks, purposes, and audiences. Students practice various conventions of standard English.

Benchmark Vocabulary

Name ______________________________

DIRECTIONS Write a sentence using each word.

roaming farthest

Responses should show contextual understanding of the word.

Write in Response to Reading

How do the images on pages 18 and 19 help you better understand the text? Use evidence from the text in your response.

Responses should use evidence from the text, including information about the reindeer pulling the sled, the traditional outfits of the Sami people, the map showing how far north the people live, and the photograph showing how light it is at midnight in the summer.

Students demonstrate contextual understanding of Benchmark Vocabulary. Students read text closely and use text evidence in their written answers.

Name ______________________________

Use Illustrations to Understand Text

DIRECTIONS Using evidence from the text, answer the following questions about pages 18–19 from *Deep Down and Other Extreme Places to Live.*

1. Look at the image on the left side of page 18. What does it show?

   It shows three men in a sled pulled by a reindeer.

2. What does this help you understand about how and why the Sami people use reindeer to pull sleds?

   Responses will vary and could include that since reindeer are plentiful, they use them instead of other animals, such as horses. Also, the reindeer look very strong.

3. Look at the image in the bottom right corner of page 19. What does it show?

   It shows a blue sky, mountains, and their reflection in water.

4. How does this image help you understand what a summer day is like for the Sami people?

   Answers should include that the sun never sets during summer nights so the days and the nights are similar.

Students analyze and respond to literary and informational text.

Name ______________________

Writing

Use Linking Words to Connect Ideas Write a paragraph using linking words and phrases to connect ideas.

Responses will vary but should include a paragraph that uses linking words and phrases to connect ideas.

Conventions

Use Regular Verbs

DIRECTIONS Complete each sentence with the correct form of the regular verb.

1. I **look** (look) at my little brother.

2. He **asks** (ask) my parents for permission to go to his room.

3. They **allow** (allow) him to leave the table.

Students write routinely for a range of tasks, purposes, and audiences. Students practice various conventions of standard English.

Name ______________________________

Benchmark Vocabulary

DIRECTIONS Write a sentence using each word.

species occasions

Responses should show contextual understanding of the word.

Write in Response to Reading

Look at the text box on page 21. What do the headings help you understand about the Sami people's use of reindeer?

Responses should use evidence from the text, including that reindeer are used for food, milk, medicine, clothing, transport, and even tools.

Students demonstrate contextual understanding of Benchmark Vocabulary. Students read text closely and use text evidence in their written answers.

Name ______________________

Use Linking Words to Connect Ideas Write a paragraph using linking words and phrases to compare and contrast two kinds of extreme communities or two things people do in an extreme community.

Responses will vary but should include linking words and phrases that help compare and contrast two extreme communities or two things people do in an extreme community.

Use Plural Subjects and Verbs

DIRECTIONS Write a sentence using each verb in the present tense with a plural subject.

1. keep **The teachers keep track of their students.**
2. throw **The boys throw the ball back and forth.**
3. stop **Monique and Susan stop at the gate.**

Students write routinely for a range of tasks, purposes, and audiences. Students practice various conventions of standard English.

Name ______________________________

Benchmark Vocabulary

DIRECTIONS Write a sentence using each word.

probably imagine normal

Responses should show contextual understanding of the word.

Write in Response to Reading

Do you think that your life might seem extreme to the people you read about in *Deep Down and Other Extreme Places to Live?* Explain your answer using evidence from the text.

Responses should use evidence from the text.

Students demonstrate contextual understanding of Benchmark Vocabulary. Students read text closely and use text evidence in their written answers.

Name ______________________________

Provide a Concluding Statement or Section Write a paragraph that concludes the piece of informative writing that you started in Lesson 4.

Responses will vary but should include a conclusion to the piece of informative writing that the student started in Lesson 4.

Review Regular Past-Tense Verbs

DIRECTIONS Complete each sentence with the correct past-tense form of the verb.

1. My mother **helped** (help) her friend move yesterday.
2. Melissa and I **packed** (pack) a few boxes.
3. Then my mother and her friend **labeled** (label) each one.

Students write routinely for a range of tasks, purposes, and audiences. Students practice various conventions of standard English.

Name ______________________

Suffixes *-ly, -ful, -ness, -less, -able, -ible*

DIRECTIONS Add the suffix ***-ly, -ful, -ness, -able, -ible,*** or ***-less*** to each base word. Write the new word on the line.

1. grace + ful = graceful
2. bare + ly = barely
3. depend + able = dependable
4. fair + ness = fairness
5. digest + ible = digestible
6. wire + less = wireless
7. rare + ly = rarely
8. neat + ness = neatness

DIRECTIONS Add the suffix ***-ly, -ful, -ness, -able, -ible,*** or ***-less*** to the base word in parentheses to complete each sentence. You may have to make a slight spelling change. Write the new word on the line.

careless **9.** A (care) mistake can cause a spill.

quickly **10.** A spill can (quick) lead to falls.

responsible **11.** We can all help by being (response).

safely **12.** If you see a spill, (safe) mop it up.

careful **13.** Be (care) to blockade any wet area.

thoughtfulness **14.** Your (thoughtful) will be appreciated.

passable **15.** The area will be (pass) again in no time.

Students apply grade-level phonics and word analysis skills.

Benchmark Vocabulary

Name ______________________________

DIRECTIONS Write a sentence using the word.

medicinal

Responses should show contextual understanding of the word.

Write in Response to Reading

DIRECTIONS Read the definitions included in the glossary on page 26. Select one or two words, and explain how each definition helps you better understand an idea in the text.

Responses may vary but should include that understanding the definition of a word will help explain what the text is about.

Students demonstrate contextual understanding of Benchmark Vocabulary. Students read text closely and use text evidence in their written answers.

Writing

Name ______________________

Take Brief Notes on Sources Choose a topic from the list provided by your teacher. Research it, take notes on the sources you find, and write down definitions of unknown words. Write those notes and definitions below or on a separate sheet of paper.

Responses will vary but should include notes and definitions taken from sources about the student's topic.

Conventions

Use Regular Past-Tense Verbs in a Sentence

DIRECTIONS Write a sentence using each verb in the past tense and with the type of subject identified.

1. fill (singular subject) **Marian filled her cup with water.**
2. fill (plural subject) **The kids filled the bags with leaves.**
3. save (singular subject) **I saved a slice of cake for you.**
4. save (plural subject) **Lisa and Nick saved two hundred dollars last month.**

Students write routinely for a range of tasks, purposes, and audiences. Students practice various conventions of standard English.

Benchmark Vocabulary

Name ____________________

DIRECTIONS Write a sentence using each word.

cities similar normal

Responses should show contextual understanding of the word.

Write in Response to Reading

Compare and contrast one type of home from *City Homes* and one type of home from *Deep Down and Other Extreme Places to Live.* How are the homes appropriate for living in a certain place? Write your answer below, on a separate sheet of paper, or in a new document.

Responses should use evidence from the text.

Students demonstrate contextual understanding of Benchmark Vocabulary. Students read text closely and use text evidence in their written answers.

Name ______________________________

Compare and Contrast

DIRECTIONS Using evidence from the texts, answer the following questions about *City Homes* and *Deep Down and Other Extreme Places to Live.*

1. *Deep Down and Other Extreme Places to Live* shows how people who live in extreme places overcome many challenges to live there. What challenges do people face in *City Homes,* and how do they overcome them?

   Responses will vary but could include that Yazd, Iran, is very hot, so people build wind catchers. People in Moscow, Russia, pump hot water through pipes to warm their houses.

2. What are some advantages and disadvantages of living in a big city?

   Responses will vary, but advantages could include that there are more places to work (such as factories), more stores, and many different things to do. A disadvantage could be that cities are crowded *(City Homes).*

3. What are some advantages and disadvantages of living in a small town or village?

   Responses will vary, but an advantage could be that they are not as crowded as cities. Disadvantages could be that there are fewer factories, no public transportation, and fewer stores.

4. Could any of the places from *Deep Down and Other Extreme Places to Live* be included in *City Homes*? Could any places in *City Homes* be included in *Deep Down and Other Extreme Places to Live*? Support your answer with evidence from the text.

   Responses will vary, but opinions should be supported with text evidence.

Students analyze and respond to literary and informational text.

Name ______________________________

Writing

Gather Information On a separate sheet of paper, write a paragraph about the topic you chose in Lesson 11. Use your notes from the previous lesson, as well as facts, details, and definitions from three sources to develop your paragraph. You may use *City Homes* and *Deep Down and Other Extreme Places to Live* as two of your sources. List your sources after the end of your paragraph.

Responses will vary but should include a paragraph containing facts, details, and definitions from three sources and a list of sources.

Conventions

Define Plural Irregular Verbs

DIRECTIONS Fill in the blanks by writing the past-tense form of each verb in parentheses.

1. They **built** (build) the house last year.
2. We **made** (make) collages in art class.
3. My sisters **became** (become) very quiet.

Students write routinely for a range of tasks, purposes, and audiences. Students practice various conventions of standard English.

Benchmark Vocabulary

Name ______________________________

DIRECTIONS Write a sentence using each word.

journey shuffled crooked drought

Responses should show contextual understanding of the word.

Write in Response to Reading

Traditions, songs, beliefs, and stories make up a culture's folklore. How can folklore do more than entertain people? Use examples from the text and your own experience to support your answer.

Responses will vary but text evidence should include that Grandma knew an old way of getting water from the roots of the acacia tree and that the old song Ramata heard might be a clue about where water could be found.

Students demonstrate contextual understanding of Benchmark Vocabulary. Students read text closely and use text evidence in their written answers.

Name ______________________________

The World's Smallest Nation

What would it be like to live on an island in the Pacific Ocean that is only about 8 square miles? How is living on an island community different? How does it affect the culture? You might ask someone who lives on the Republic of Nauru (nah-OO-roo).

Nauru sits just south of the equator. Its closest neighbor is a whopping 200 miles away! About 3,000 years ago, the first people migrated to the island from Micronesia and Polynesia. They lived in tribes or groups much like the Native Americans of North America did. Nauru had a unique culture and enjoyed peace for centuries.

In 1798, a British captain of a whaling ship saw Nauru on his way to China. Later, the first Europeans arrived. They brought new ideas, weapons, and war. From the 1800s to the mid-1900s, different European countries, Japan, and Australia took control of Nauru. They used its resources for trade and influenced Nauru's culture and community. Finally, Nauru gained its freedom in 1968.

Today, Nauru is home to many different cultures because of its history. More than half of the people speak the Nauruan language. English is also spoken, but less than 10 percent of the people are European. Other groups include Pacific Islanders and Chinese. As an independent nation, Nauru's culture is still unique. Its culture is traditional with a blend of other cultures from around the world.

Students read text closely to determine what the text says.

Name ________________________________

Gather Evidence What additional information can you learn from the pictures and labels? Circle information from the text that corresponds with the pictures and labels.

Responses will vary but could include where Nauru is located on the globe, what the land looks like, and what the flag looks like.

Gather Evidence: Extend Your Ideas Write a sentence explaining how the pictures contribute to what is conveyed by the text.

Responses may vary but may include that the pictures show where Nauru is located, that it is an island, and that Europeans damaged some of Nauru's land when they took resources.

Ask Questions What questions would you ask someone who had visited Nauru? Circle information in the text that answers these questions.

Responses will vary but should use text evidence.

Ask Questions: Extend Your Ideas What questions would you ask someone who had visited Nauru that are not answered in the text? Research your questions and write 1–2 sentences discussing each one.

Responses will vary.

Make Your Case What are two interesting differences between Nauru and where you live? Why do you think those differences are interesting?

Responses will vary but should include text evidence about Nauru.

Make Your Case: Extend Your Ideas Write 2–3 sentences using information you researched about Nauru and comparing it to where you live. Discuss your results with a partner.

Responses will vary.

Students read text closely to determine what the text says.

Name ______________________

Writing

Sort Evidence Sort evidence for an essay that will compare your own way of life to the research you have done on other communities. Sort your notes from Lessons 11 and 12 into at least three categories. Use the space below or a separate sheet of paper.

Responses will vary but should include evidence sorted into three or more categories.

Conventions

How Plural Irregular Verbs Function

DIRECTIONS Rewrite each sentence below in the past tense.

1. They run five miles every day. **They ran five miles every day.**

2. Myra and Frank are outside. **Myra and Frank were outside.**

3. Felix and Thomas go to practice every Tuesday. **Felix and Thomas went to practice every Tuesday.**

Students write routinely for a range of tasks, purposes, and audiences. Students practice various conventions of standard English.

Benchmark Vocabulary

Name ______________________________

DIRECTIONS Write a sentence using each word.

desert limit navigate celebrate

Responses should show contextual understanding of the word.

Write in Response to Reading

Did Ramata want Grandma to go with her? Why or why not? Use evidence from the text to support your answer.

Responses should use evidence from the text, including that Ramata had no choice but to agree that Grandma should go with them. Ramata admitted that Grandma's knowledge of the old ways might be a help in their quest.

Students demonstrate contextual understanding of Benchmark Vocabulary. Students read text closely and use text evidence in their written answers.

Name ______________________________

Plan and Prewrite Create an outline for your essay comparing and contrasting your way of life with the way of life in other communities. First, use print and reliable digital sources to gather additional information. Then, use this information and the information you collected in Lessons 11–13 to make an outline for an essay. Write your outline on a separate sheet of paper.

Responses will vary but should be an outline comparing and contrasting the student's way of life with another culture's way of life.

Use Plural Irregular Verbs in a Sentence

DIRECTIONS Write a sentence using each irregular verb in the past tense with a plural subject.

1. get **The cats got their dinner at seven o'clock.**
2. catch **Five kids caught the flu.**
3. eat **The friends ate lunch together.**

Students write routinely for a range of tasks, purposes, and audiences. Students practice various conventions of standard English.

Benchmark Vocabulary

Name ____________________

DIRECTIONS Write a sentence using each word.

natural spring

Responses should show contextual understanding of the word.

Write in Response to Reading

Find an unfamiliar word in the text. Write what you think the word means and what clues in the text helped you come up with that definition. Then explain how this word adds meaning to the story.

Responses should use evidence from the text.

Students demonstrate contextual understanding of Benchmark Vocabulary. Students read text closely and use text evidence in their written answers.

Name ____________________

Determine Word Meaning

DIRECTIONS Using evidence from the text, answer the following questions about *The Song of Sky and Sand.*

1. What does *drowned out* mean on page 8?

   Drowned out **means being covered by louder sounds.**

2. What clues in the text help you understand the meaning of *drowned out?* Explain how they help you understand the word's meaning.

   Responses will vary but could include that the phrases "cart rattled past" and "by the wheels of Ramata's donkey cart" help show that the cart makes a lot of noise, which is why the words of the song are "drowned out."

3. What does *cry* mean in the second sentence on page 33? What does *cries* mean in the last sentence on page 36?

   cry **on p. 33: to weep;** ***cries*** **on p. 36: loud noises**

4. What clues in the text help you understand the meaning of *cry* on page 33? Explain how they help you understand its meaning.

   Responses will vary but could include that "slumped back on the rock" and "stared dry-eyed" help to show that Ramata is disappointed but ***not*** **tearing up.**

5. What clues in the text help you understand the meaning of *cries* on page 36? Explain how they help you understand its meaning.

   Responses will vary but could include that the phrase "of joy" shows that the people's cries are not sad.

Students analyze and respond to literary and informational text.

Writing

Name ______________________________

Draft an Essay Use the outline you made in Lesson 14 to draft a compare-and-contrast essay about your way of life and the way of life in other communities. Write your draft on a separate sheet of paper.

Responses will vary but should be a draft of an essay comparing and contrasting the student's way of life and the way of life in other communities.

Conventions

Use Past-Tense Irregular Verbs in a Sentence

DIRECTIONS Write a sentence using each verb in the past tense.

1. give **I gave her chocolates for Valentine's Day.**
2. spring **The cat sprang onto the bed.**
3. know **The students knew all the answers to the test.**

Students write routinely for a range of tasks, purposes, and audiences. Students practice various conventions of standard English.

Name ______________________________

Consonant Patterns *wr, kn, gn, st, mb*

DIRECTIONS Choose the word in parentheses with the silent consonant, as in *wr, kn, st, mb,* or *gn,* to complete each sentence. Write the word on the line.

climb **1.** It was a perfect winter day for a (climb/hike).

knapsack **2.** Theo packed water and snacks in a (cooler/knapsack).

knit **3.** Brin handed Theo a (knit/new) cap.

design **4.** She grabbed the scarf with the zigzag (checks/design).

wrapped **5.** She (wrapped/threw) another scarf around Theo's neck.

fastening **6.** Theo began (fastening/dusting) the snaps on his jacket.

Listen **7.** Then someone said, "(Listen/Answer) to the radio!"

signs **8.** There were (signs/signals) that a big storm was coming.

knew **9.** Theo and Brin (knew/realized) their plans had to change.

DIRECTIONS Circle each word in the Word Bank that has a silent consonant. Write the circled words in alphabetical order on the lines below.

Word Bank

gnaw	relax	castle	wriggle	basket	water
trap	numb	next	comb	knot	humid

10. castle **13.** comb

11. gnaw **14.** knot

12. numb **15.** wriggle

Students apply grade-level phonics and word analysis skills.

Name ______________________

Benchmark Vocabulary

DIRECTIONS Write a sentence using each word.

extreme journey

Responses should show contextual understanding of the word.

Write in Response to Reading

Write a paragraph comparing and contrasting how people use animals to survive in each of the texts.

Responses should use evidence from the text, including that in *City Homes*, people do not need to use animals to survive; they have stores and do not have herd animals. In *The Song of Sky and Sand* and *Deep Down and Other Extreme Places to Live,* people use animals to help carry things and as transportation. In *Deep Down*, many people also use animals as food (the Afar and the Sami).

Students demonstrate contextual understanding of Benchmark Vocabulary. Students read text closely and use text evidence in their written answers.

Name ______________________________

Revise an Essay On a separate sheet of paper, make revisions to your compare-and-contrast essay from Lesson 15. Look for information you left out or may want to cut from your essay.

Responses will vary but should include a revised compare-and-contrast essay with information added or removed.

Use Conventional Spelling

DIRECTIONS For each word and suffix combination, spell the word they create correctly.

Example: swim + ing = swimming.

1. mop + ed = **mopped**
2. hope + ful = **hopeful**
3. salty + ness = **saltiness**

Students write routinely for a range of tasks, purposes, and audiences. Students practice various conventions of standard English.

Benchmark Vocabulary

Name ______________________________

DIRECTIONS Write a sentence using each word.

townhouses suburbs apartments desert

Responses should show contextual understanding of the word.

Write in Response to Reading

Think about how the illustrations in *The Song of Sky and Sand* and the photographs in *City Homes* helped you understand the text. Did you find the illustrations in *The Song of Sky and Sand* or the photographs in *City Homes* more useful? Explain your answer using evidence from the texts.

Responses will vary but should include that the photographs in *City Homes* are more realistic while the illustrations in *The Song of Sky and Sand* may not be as realistic but are more imaginative and help readers "see" the story.

Students demonstrate contextual understanding of Benchmark Vocabulary. Students read text closely and use text evidence in their written answers.

Name ________________________________

Edit an Essay Find a partner, and then trade and edit each other's compare-and-contrast essays. Look for errors in spelling, grammar, and punctuation. Also note places where the wording is awkward and where more or different details might improve the writing. Mark any errors or suggestions in a different colored pen or pencil, and discuss them with your partner.

Responses will vary but should include essays with corrections and suggestions for improvements.

Use Spelling Patterns and Generalizations

DIRECTIONS Circle the correctly spelled word in parentheses.

1. I saw a lot of (monkeys / monkeies) at the zoo. **monkeys**
2. (Pik / Pick) fresh ingredients at the market. **Pick**
3. She (trys / tries) to study for an hour every night. **tries**

Students write routinely for a range of tasks, purposes, and audiences. Students practice various conventions of standard English.

Benchmark Vocabulary

Name ____________________

DIRECTIONS Write a sentence using each word.

provide concrete streetcars

Responses should show contextual understanding of the word.

Write in Response to Reading

How have *City Homes, Deep Down and Other Extreme Places to Live,* and *The Song of Sky and Sand* helped you understand the similarities and differences between the communities of the world? Use evidence from the texts to support your answer.

Responses should use evidence from the texts, including that communities are not that different even if they are in different areas of the world. People live in cities because there is work and food and shelter (*City Homes*). In remote areas, communities work together to help find necessities, like food and water. This is seen in *The Song of Sky and Sand* and in *Deep Down and Other Extreme Places to Live,* where the people, including the Afar and Sami, work together to provide their communities with what they need.

Students demonstrate contextual understanding of Benchmark Vocabulary. Students read text closely and use text evidence in their written answers.

Name ______________________________

Compare and Contrast

DIRECTIONS Using evidence from the texts, answer the following questions about *City Homes, Deep Down and Other Extreme Places to Live*, and *The Song of Sky and Sand*.

1. How does each text show the connection between people's surroundings and their culture?

   Responses will vary but could include that in a dry climate, people sing songs about where to find water (*The Song of Sky and Sand*), use their herding animals for food and clothing (like the Sami in *Deep Down*), and design homes for the weather, such as in Yazd, Iran (*City Homes*).

2. Which two communities from the three texts have the most similarities? Explain your answer using evidence from the texts.

   Responses will vary but could include the Afar and the Sami. Both are nomadic and have movable homes. Both groups rely on animals for transportation, though the Sami now also use snowmobiles.

3. Which two communities from the three texts have the most differences? Explain your answer using evidence from the texts.

   Responses will vary but could include the people in northern Mali and the Sami. The Sami live in very cold climates, and the people in Mali live in a very hot and dry climate. The Mali are not nomadic, but the Sami are.

4. Which text was the most interesting to read? Explain your answer using evidence from the text.

   Responses will vary.

Students analyze and respond to literary and informational text.

Name ______________________________

Publish and Present Your Writing Write an edited version of your compare-and-contrast essay on a separate sheet of paper. Then publish your compare-and-contrast essay and present it to the class.

Responses will vary but should include an edited version of the student's compare-and-contrast essay that will be published and presented to the class.

Consult Reference Materials to Check Words

DIRECTIONS Read the following sentences, and use reference materials to check the spelling of each underlined word. Write *correct* on the line if the word is spelled correctly, and identify the source you used to check the spelling. If the spelling is incorrect, write the correct spelling, and identify the source you used to check the spelling.

1. <u>Soul</u> is the capital of South Korea. **Seoul**
2. Gumbo is a traditional <u>Creole</u> dish. **correct**
3. Lauren had a bad <u>atitude</u>, so no one talked to her. **attitude**

Students write routinely for a range of tasks, purposes, and audiences. Students practice various conventions of standard English.

Name ______________________________

Irregular Plurals

DIRECTIONS Use the plural form of each word in parentheses to complete each sentence. Write the word on the line.

mice 1. Timmy wasn't like the other (mouse).

teeth 2. He was missing all his (tooth).

loaves 3. He couldn't chew the (loaf) of bread.

feet 4. Using his (foot) to tear off small pieces took too long.

women 5. Of course, the (woman) would not help him.

men 6. Timmy hid from the cleaning (man), too.

children 7. At last, Timmy saw (child) dropping crumbs.

shelves 8. Now he stores crumbs on (shelf), to eat whenever he wants.

DIRECTIONS Write the plural form of each word below.

9. wife wives

10. wolf wolves

11. scarf scarves

12. hero heroes

13. cuff cuffs

14. calf calves

15. deer deer

16. elf elves

17. half halves

18. goose geese

19. knife knives

20. sheep sheep

Students apply grade-level phonics and word analysis skills.

Name ________________________________

Benchmark Vocabulary

DIRECTIONS Write a sentence using the word.

canyon

Responses should show contextual understanding of the word.

Write in Response to Reading

Read pages 7–11. Keep in mind the order of events of the story the grandfather tells the boy. Write an explanatory paragraph that summarizes how the characters contributed to the sequence of events in the excerpt. Keep the events in the order they appear in the text.

Responses should use evidence from the text, including that Thomas's questions about Grandfather's childhood eventually lead to Grandfather's story about Melvin later in the text. Also, as the characters are sitting in darkness, Thomas notices how much more he can hear when he is "just listening." He will be listening to Grandfather's story in this way.

Students demonstrate contextual understanding of Benchmark Vocabulary. Students read text closely and use text evidence in their written answers.

Name ______________________________

Contributions of Illustrations to a Text

DIRECTIONS Using evidence from the text, answer the following questions about pages 6–11 of *Knots on a Counting Rope.*

1. What does the illustration on pages 6–7 tell you about the characters that the text does not?

   It shows what the characters look like. The characters are holding a rope with knots.

2. How do the characters feel on pages 8–9? What clues in the illustration support your opinion?

   They are happy. Both characters are smiling.

3. On page 11, what does it say the great blue horses gave the boy? How does the illustration help show that information?

   The horses gave him the strength to live. In the illustration, the baby is reaching up like he is getting strength from the blue horse.

Students analyze and respond to literary and informational text.

Name ______________________

Writing

State an Opinion Think about a topic you feel strongly about. Write a paragraph in which you present your opinion and give reasons and examples that support your opinion.

Responses will vary but should include a topic, the student's opinion about the topic, and reasons and examples that support the student's opinion.

Conventions

Function of Nouns

DIRECTIONS Underline the noun that serves as the subject of the sentence. Then identify whether the noun names a person, place, animal, or thing.

1. The orange cat leapt from the cold, hard floor to the soft, warm bed. **animal**
2. Two yellow buses drove down the road toward the school. **thing**
3. Julia is watching her children from the window. **person**

Students write routinely for a range of tasks, purposes, and audiences. Students practice various conventions of standard English.

Benchmark Vocabulary

Name ______________________________

DIRECTIONS Write a sentence using each word.

ceremony sweep

Responses should show contextual understanding of the word.

Write in Response to Reading

Reread pages 12–16 of *Knots on a Counting Rope.* Write an explanatory paragraph that touches on the literal and nonliteral uses of words and phrases on those pages. Use the vocabulary words and evidence from the text to support your writing.

Responses will vary, but students should discuss the literal and nonliteral meanings of these phrases: "kitchen clock, very excited," "Automobile tires swished," "Horns honked and hollered," "A siren whined."

Students demonstrate contextual understanding of Benchmark Vocabulary. Students read text closely and use text evidence in their written answers.

Name ______________________________

Writing

Write About Reading On a separate sheet of paper, write a short opinion essay about *Knots on a Counting Rope.* State an opinion about the book, state an opinion about one or both of the characters, and support your opinions with reasons and examples from the text.

Responses will vary but should include the student's opinions about *Knots on a Counting Rope* and one or both of its characters. It should also include reasons and examples from the text that support the student's opinions.

Conventions

Function of Nouns in Sentences

DIRECTIONS Circle the nouns in each sentence. Tell whether each noun is the subject, direct object, or indirect object of the sentence.

1. Cho quickly threw the baseball. ***Cho* is the subject of the sentence. *Baseball* is the direct object of the sentence.**

2. Sarah sent Amare an e-mail. ***Sarah* is the subject of the sentence. *E-mail* is the direct object of the sentence. *Amare* is the indirect object of the sentence.**

3. Nate cooked dinner. ***Nate* is the subject of the sentence. *Dinner* is the direct object of the sentence.**

Students write routinely for a range of tasks, purposes, and audiences. Students practice various conventions of standard English.

Benchmark Vocabulary

Name ________________________________

DIRECTIONS Write a sentence using each word.

traced surround

Responses should show contextual understanding of the word.

Write in Response to Reading

Read page 20 of *Knots on a Counting Rope.* Write a paragraph that touches on the literal and nonliteral uses of words and phrases on this page. Use the vocabulary words and evidence from the text to support your writing.

Responses will vary, but students should discuss the literal and nonliteral meanings of these phrases: "boy walks in beauty," "story by heart," "cross the dark mountains," "My love will surround you," "strength of blue horses."

Students demonstrate contextual understanding of Benchmark Vocabulary. Students read text closely and use text evidence in their written answers.

Name ______________________________

We Need New Tornado Warnings!

Over 1,200 tornadoes touched down in the United States in 2010. Sirens are often used to alert people of the possibility of a tornado. I think tornado sirens are now obsolete. They should be replaced.

Obviously, it is important to warn people of danger. In the past, bells were hung high in towers to warn people. When communities began to use electricity in the 1930s, sirens replaced bells as the warning signal.

I grew up listening to the blares of tornado siren tests. They happened every Wednesday morning at 10:00. Clear, sunny days in the summer were suddenly interrupted with a deafening siren. I got used to ignoring them.

Also, tornado sirens can cause panic in people who aren't used to them. One time, a visitor heard the Wednesday morning siren test. She panicked. She ran inside for shelter. There was not a rain cloud in sight. Such is the power of a tornado siren!

There are better ways to warn people about tornadoes. By the 1960s, radio and television were used as warning systems. With the Internet, cell phones, and smartphones, we now have fast ways of tracking a storm. This technology can even help you locate the nearest tornado shelter! With a siren, you have only a warning and not much else.

Finally, sirens can cost lots of money. Let's spend the money we save from not using sirens on sharing information. We can make certain that emergency weather information is communicated through the technology of today.

Students read text closely to determine what the text says.

Name ______________________________

Gather Evidence Circle the clues in the text that tell you the writer is giving both facts and opinions. **See annotations on previous page.**

Gather Evidence: Extend Your Ideas Did you circle "I think"? Explain why this is a good opinion clue.

Responses may vary but could include that "I think" is not a statement of fact; it is an opinion statement.

Ask Questions Underline two observations the narrator makes about siren tests. What two questions would you ask an expert about tornado warnings?

See annotations on previous page. Responses will vary.

Ask Questions: Extend Your Ideas What would you ask someone who has survived a tornado?

Responses may vary.

Make Your Case Do you think the writer does a good job of stating an opinion and giving reasons to support it? Underline examples from the text that support your opinion about the writer's skills.

Responses may vary.

Make Your Case: Extend Your Ideas On a separate piece of paper, write at least 3–4 sentences stating your opinions about the writer's skills. Make sure to give reasons to support it. Trade papers with a partner and discuss what you have written. **Responses may vary.**

Students read text closely to determine what the text says.

Name ______________________________

Writing About the Unit Topic Write an opinion about the relationship between the grandfather and grandson in *Knots on a Counting Rope.* Support your opinion with reasons and evidence from the text.

Responses will vary but should include the student's opinion about the relationship between the grandfather and the grandson, as well as reasons and evidence that support the student's opinion.

Functions of Pronouns

DIRECTIONS Underline the pronoun in each sentence. Then write whether the pronoun is the subject, direct object, or indirect object of the sentence.

1. Lily bought me a book. **In this sentence, *me* is an indirect object.**

2. She said the book was really interesting. ***She* is the subject of this sentence.**

3. Lily's mother likes it too. ***It* is the direct object of this sentence.**

Students write routinely for a range of tasks, purposes, and audiences. Students practice various conventions of standard English.

Benchmark Vocabulary

Name ______________________________

DIRECTIONS Write a sentence using each word.

canyon traced

Responses should show contextual understanding of the word.

Write in Response to Reading

Read pages 17–18 of *Knots on a Counting Rope.* Write a paragraph that explains the boy's traits, motivations, and feelings.

Responses should use evidence from the text, including that he taught the horse to race, and he was afraid until his Grandfather called to him to "trust your darkness!" Then he raced "with all of his heart."

Students demonstrate contextual understanding of Benchmark Vocabulary. Students read text closely and use text evidence in their written answers.

Writing

Name ______________________________

Introduce a Topic Write a few sentences introducing this topic: How can relationships between people in different generations have an impact on a person's life?

Responses will vary but should include sentences that introduce the topic of how relationships between people in different generations can have an impact on a person's life.

Conventions

Use Pronouns as Sentence Subjects

DIRECTIONS In each pair of sentences below, circle the pronoun that serves as the subject of a sentence. Then underline the noun(s) the pronoun replaces.

1. The sugar was not in the pantry. It was on the kitchen counter.
2. Rhonda and Brian are driving from Maryland to Oregon. They will stop and visit museums along the way.
3. Melissa will not stay with her aunt this summer. She will work at the mall.

Students write routinely for a range of tasks, purposes, and audiences. Students practice various conventions of standard English.

Benchmark Vocabulary

Name ______________________________

DIRECTIONS Write a sentence using the word.

fluttering

Responses should show contextual understanding of the word.

Write in Response to Reading

Read page 6 of the text. Do you think it's hard to imagine a grown-up as a little child? Why or why not? Use evidence from the text to support your answer.

Responses will vary but should use evidence from the text, including that Thomas didn't believe that a young boy could grow up to be an old man. Thomas believed he'd always be a boy so it was hard to understand that Grandfather had been a boy once ("probably at the beginning of the world").

Students demonstrate contextual understanding of Benchmark Vocabulary. Students read text closely and use text evidence in their written answers.

Name ______________________________

Figurative Language

DIRECTIONS Using evidence from the text, answer the following questions about pages 9–13 from *Storm in the Night.*

1. On page 9, the narrator states, "Thomas had a chin as smooth as a peach." How does this help you understand the way Thomas's chin feels?

   The comparison to a peach helps me understand that Thomas's chin is very soft.

2. On page 9, the narrator states, "Grandfather had a voice like a tuba. Thomas's voice was like a penny whistle." What does this description mean?

   Grandfather has a deep voice, and Thomas has a high voice.

3. Read page 12. The author uses the words *ping, tick,* and *bong* in her descriptions of clocks and bells. Why does the author use these words? What do they sound like?

   The author uses these words to describe the sounds of the clocks and the bells. These words sound like the sounds they are describing.

Students analyze and respond to literary and informational text.

Name ______________________________

State an Opinion Complete the sentences below to write four opinion statements about the topic you introduced in Lesson 4. Remember that you are writing about how relationships between people from different generations can have an impact on a person's life.

1. I like ______________________________.
2. I do not like ______________________________.
3. My favorite ______________ is ______________.
4. I like ______________ better than ______________.

Responses will vary but should include four opinion statements about the topic the student introduced in Lesson 4.

Use Pronouns as Objects

DIRECTIONS Circle the correct pronoun to complete each sentence.

1. Jack asked (she / her) for help lifting the box. **her**
2. My father gave (he / him) the computer. **him**
3. Mrs. Smith drove (they / them) to the movie theater. **them**

Students write routinely for a range of tasks, purposes, and audiences. Students practice various conventions of standard English.

Name ______________________________

R-Controlled Vowels *ir, er, ur, ear, or, ar, ore, oar*

DIRECTIONS Circle the words in the Word Bank that have the vowel sound **/er/** as in ***bird, her, turn, earn,*** and ***work.*** Then write the words you circled under the word that has the same vowel spelling.

Word Bank

burst	hear	corn	dear	early	there	stern
fire	flare	heart	girl	hurry	learn	pear
perch	skirt	tire	torn	world	worm	

bird
1. girl
2. skirt

her
3. stern
4. perch

turn
5. burst
6. hurry

earn
7. early
8. learn

work
9. world
10. worm

DIRECTIONS Circle the word that has the same vowel sound as the first word. Then write a sentence that uses the word you circled.

11. farm frame (dart) rare

____

12. short hoot (horn) shot

____

13. core cone to (shore)

____

14. board boat proud (roar)

____

Students apply grade-level phonics and word analysis skills.

Benchmark Vocabulary

Name ______________________________

DIRECTIONS Write a sentence using each word.

brandishing commanded interrupting ashamed

Responses should show contextual understanding of the word.

Write in Response to Reading

Look at the illustration on page 26 and read page 27. Write an explanatory paragraph about how the illustration on page 26 contributes to the grandfather's story on page 27.

Responses should use evidence from the text, including that the boy in the picture looks frightened and the man looks very, very tall to the boy. In the picture, the man also seems to be scolding the boy.

Students demonstrate contextual understanding of Benchmark Vocabulary. Students read text closely and use text evidence in their written answers.

Name ______________________________

Contributions of Illustrations to a Text

DIRECTIONS Using evidence from the text, answer the following questions about pages 16–26 from *Storm in the Night.*

1. Look at the illustration on page 16. Then read page 17. Which strong words from the text help tell about the sights and sounds of the storm around them as Thomas and his grandfather sit on the swing?

   Responses will vary but could include words such as *whooped, windily, brandishing, tearing, drenched, splashed, clattered, boomed,* and *stabbed.*

2. On page 19, what can you tell from Grandfather and Thomas's relationship by looking at how they are sitting together? Explain.

   They are sitting close. They are comfortable, and they look like they are relaxed and get along well.

3. Read the last part of page 21 beginning with the sentence, "So there we were, the two of us, . . ." Then look at the illustration on page 22. How can readers tell that the large illustration is what Grandfather is thinking in the past?

   Grandfather and Thomas are still shown in a small illustration on page 23, so readers know he is telling the story.

4. How does the illustration on page 26 change the mood of the story? Which details in the illustration convey this mood?

   The man is drawn very large with lots of dark shadows, and readers cannot see his face. Grandfather looks small and scared.

Students analyze and respond to literary and informational text.

Name ______________________________

Reasons to Support an Opinion Write reasons that support the four opinions you stated in Lesson 5.

Responses will vary but should include reasons that support the student's opinions from Lesson 5.

Functions of Adjectives

DIRECTIONS Circle the adjective in each sentence. Then underline the noun that it describes.

1. The kids ran through the dirty puddle of water.
2. The playful dog kept jumping on the sofa to get Lisa's attention.
3. New Orleans is very hot during the summer.

Students write routinely for a range of tasks, purposes, and audiences. Students practice various conventions of standard English.

Benchmark Vocabulary

Name ______________________________

DIRECTIONS Write a sentence using the word.

mutterings

Responses should show contextual understanding of the word.

Write in Response to Reading

Write a paragraph that explains why you think the author used nonliteral meanings in the text. Use text evidence to support your answer.

Responses will vary but should use text evidence to support their opinions, such as that nonliteral language is more descriptive and interesting. "The storm was spent" helps the reader see that the violent and full-of-energy storm is now exhausted. That is far more interesting to read than "the storm was almost over."

Students demonstrate contextual understanding of Benchmark Vocabulary. Students read text closely and use text evidence in their written answers.

Name ______________________

Literal and Nonliteral Meanings

DIRECTIONS Using evidence from the text, answer the following questions about page 28 of *Storm in the Night.*

1. On page 28, the narrator states, "The storm was spent." What does *spent* mean in this sentence?

   It was done. It had used up its strength.

2. What words or phrases around *spent* help readers understand its meaning?

   The next sentence describes what *spent* means: "There were only flickers of lightning, mutterings of thunder, and a little patter of rain."

3. Read the last paragraph on page 28. What does *mutterings* mean?

   low grumbles, like someone talking under his or her breath

4. Does the author really mean that the thunder is muttering? Explain.

   No, comparing the sound of the thunder to the sound of a person muttering helps readers understand that the storm was moving away and was almost over.

Students analyze and respond to literary and informational text.

Writing

Name ______________________________

Support an Opinion with Reasons Select one of the following opinions:

1. Bringing lunch from home is/is not better than buying it at the cafeteria.

2. *Storm in the Night* is/is not a good book for very young children.

On the lines below, write the opinion you selected, reasons that will support it, and facts and details that help explain those reasons.

Responses will vary but should include the opinion the student selected, as well as reasons, facts, and details that will support it.

Conventions

Functions of Adjectives in Sentences

DIRECTIONS Rewrite each sentence, adding at least one adjective.

1. The boy walked cautiously across the bridge.

The boy walked cautiously across the old bridge.

2. Monica picked the flowers from her yard.

Monica picked the red flowers from her small yard.

3. The cat ran under the house.

The terrified cat ran under the house.

Students write routinely for a range of tasks, purposes, and audiences. Students practice various conventions of standard English.

Benchmark Vocabulary

Name ____________________

DIRECTIONS Write a sentence using each word.

fluttering commanded

Responses should show contextual understanding of the word.

Write in Response to Reading

Write an explanatory paragraph that summarizes the sequence of events in the story.

Sequence of events in the story: lights go out in the storm, Thomas and Grandfather sit on the porch swing and smell the air, Thomas says he's not scared, Grandfather tells the story about how he was scared of storms when he was a boy and how he lost and found his dog during a storm, the storm dies down, Thomas admits he was a little scared, the lights come on, they go to bed.

Students demonstrate contextual understanding of Benchmark Vocabulary. Students read text closely and use text evidence in their written answers.

Name ______________________________

Writing

Create an Organizational Structure Plan and organize the reasons and supporting details for an opinion piece. First, choose one of your opinion statements from Lesson 5 and the reasons that support that opinion from Lesson 6. Next, on a separate sheet of paper, take notes on evidence from the text that relates to your opinion and reasons. Then, create an outline to organize your reasons and supporting details. Finally, write your opinion essay, using your outline as a guide for structuring it.

Responses will vary but should include notes on evidence from the text that relates to the student's opinion and reasons, an outline that organizes the reasons and details that support the student's opinion, and a draft of an opinion essay based on that outline.

Conventions

Use Adjectives

DIRECTIONS Write sentences that use adjectives to describe parts of *Storm in the Night.*

1. **Responses will vary. Inside, it was dark except for the orange flames of the fire.**

2. **Responses will vary. The loud, bright lightning split the tree in half.**

3. **Responses will vary. Grandfather was very scared.**

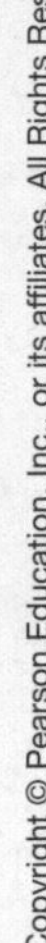

Students write routinely for a range of tasks, purposes, and audiences. Students practice various conventions of standard English.

Benchmark Vocabulary

Name ______________________________

DIRECTIONS Write a sentence using the word.

brandishing

Responses should show contextual understanding of the word.

Write in Response to Reading

Write a paragraph explaining whether or not you think Grandfather made the right choice in telling this story to Thomas. Use evidence from the text to support your answer.

Responses should use evidence from the text.

Students demonstrate contextual understanding of Benchmark Vocabulary. Students read text closely and use text evidence in their written answers.

Name ______________________________

Use Linking Words and Phrases to Connect Ideas On a separate sheet of paper, add linking words and phrases to connect your opinion and reasons in the opinion piece you wrote in Lesson 8.

Responses will vary but should include an opinion piece with linking words and phrases that connect the student's opinion to his or her reasons.

Form Comparative and Superlative Adjectives

DIRECTIONS Complete each sentence with an appropriate comparative or superlative adjective.

1. Ringo's eyes were **wider** than Thomas's eyes. **Answers will vary.**
2. The thunder was the **loudest** thunder Thomas had ever heard. **Answers will vary.**
3. The green coat is **more expensive** than the blue coat. **Answers will vary.**

Students write routinely for a range of tasks, purposes, and audiences. Students practice various conventions of standard English.

Benchmark Vocabulary

Name ______________________

DIRECTIONS Write a sentence using each word.

ceremony interrupting

Responses should show contextual understanding of the word.

Write in Response to Reading

Read pages 18–28 in *Storm in the Night* and pages 8–13 in *Knots on a Counting Rope*. Compare and contrast the range of feelings experienced by the grandfathers in the telling of their stories. Use text evidence to support your response.

Responses should use evidence from the text, including that in *Storm in the Night*, Grandfather tells a story about his childhood when he was scared during a storm. Grandfather says, "I was just as afraid of storms as he [Melvin] was." He helps Thomas see that being afraid is normal. In *Knots on a Counting Rope*, the Grandfather was also afraid; he was worried about the child being born. His story is about the boy's life and how being blind doesn't stop the boy from doing things, like racing his horse. Both stories are about fear and love, and overcoming obstacles.

Students demonstrate contextual understanding of Benchmark Vocabulary. Students read text closely and use text evidence in their written answers.

Writing

Name ________________________

Provide a Concluding Statement Write a concluding statement for the opinion piece you began in Lesson 8.

Responses will vary but should include a concluding statement.

Conventions

Using Irregular Comparatives and Superlatives

DIRECTIONS Complete each sentence with the correct form of *bad*. Explain why it is correct.

1. The last stab of lightning was the worst of the night.

It compares the flash of lightning to all the others before it.

2. That flash of lightning was bad.

The lightning is not being compared to any other lightning.

3. The lightning I just saw was worse than the one I saw earlier. It compares the lightning to one other flash of lightning.

Students write routinely for a range of tasks, purposes, and audiences. Students practice various conventions of standard English.

Name ______________________

Prefixes *pre-, mid-, over-, bi-, out-, de-*

DIRECTIONS Add the prefix ***pre-, mid-, over-, out-***, or ***de-*** to each base word.

1. over- + load = overload
2. out- + going = outgoing
3. pre- + paid = prepaid
4. mid- + point = midpoint
5. de- + code = decode

DIRECTIONS Choose the word from the Word Bank that best fits the definition, and write the word on the line.

Word Bank

bicycle	midweek	outburst	defrost	prefix

prefix **6.** a word part added to the beginning of a word

bicycle **7.** a vehicle with two wheels

outburst **8.** sudden display of emotion

midweek **9.** the middle of the week

defrost **10.** to thaw something that is frozen

DIRECTIONS Add the prefix ***pre-, mid-, over-, out-***, or ***bi-*** to the base word in parentheses to complete each sentence. You will use each prefix just once. Write the word on the line.

preschool **11.** Elena began collecting rocks in (school).

outlast **12.** She knew this hobby would (last) any other hobby.

overlook **13.** It is easy to (look) special rocks in bright sunlight.

bicolor **14.** She found a (color) rock one day, however.

midnight **15.** Finding colorful rocks at (night) is nearly impossible.

Students apply grade-level phonics and word analysis skills.

Benchmark Vocabulary

Name ______________________________

DIRECTIONS Write a sentence using each word.

hitched stubborn

Responses should show contextual understanding of the word.

Write in Response to Reading

Read pages 26–27 from "Growing Up." Write a few sentences about your opinion on Babe and Paul becoming friends and working together. Support your writing using text evidence.

Responses should use evidence from the text, including that Babe and Paul "made a good team."

Students demonstrate contextual understanding of Benchmark Vocabulary. Students read text closely and use text evidence in their written answers.

Name ______________________________

Provide a Concluding Section Expand your concluding statement from Lesson 10 into a concluding section for your opinion piece. First, review your work, and then write a conclusion of at least three sentences that restates the main ideas of your essay (your opinion and reasons).

Responses will vary but should include at least three sentences that restate the main ideas (the student's opinion and reasons) in the student's opinion piece.

Use Comparative and Superlative Adjectives

DIRECTIONS Write a sentence about *Paul Bunyan* with each adjective.

1. younger **Answers will vary.**
   Babe was younger than Paul Bunyan.

2. most powerful **Answers will vary.**
   Babe was the most powerful ox of all.

3. best **Answers will vary.**
   Paul Bunyan was the best lumberjack of his time.

Students write routinely for a range of tasks, purposes, and audiences. Students practice various conventions of standard English.

Benchmark Vocabulary

Name ____________________

DIRECTIONS Write a sentence using the word.

comfortable

Responses should show contextual understanding of the word.

Write in Response to Reading

Read page 28 from "Starting Out." Write your opinion on how well the illustration helps readers see the trees and lumberjacks from Paul's point of view. Support your writing using text evidence.

Responses should use evidence from the text, including that Paul was large even compared to the trees. He towers over the other lumberjack in the illustration.

Students demonstrate contextual understanding of Benchmark Vocabulary. Students read text closely and use text evidence in their written answers.

Name ______________________________

Contributions of Illustrations to a Text

DIRECTIONS Using evidence from the text, answer the following questions about pages 28–31 of *Paul Bunyan.*

1. Look at the illustration on page 28. How does it help you understand why Babe can help Paul by pulling trees into stacks?

   In the illustration, Babe looks big and strong, which helps explain why Babe could help Paul with such hard work.

2. Look at the illustration on page 29. What does it help you better understand about the Elmers?

   Responses will vary but could include that the illustration helps the reader understand how big and strong the Elmers are.

3. Look at the illustration on page 29.What does it help you better understand about the way the Elmers cut down trees?

   Responses will vary but could include that the illustration helps the reader understand that the Elmers are very skilled axmen.

4. Look at the illustrations on pages 30 and 31.What do the illustrations help you understand about the environment in the dining hall?

   Responses will vary but could include that the dining hall was very busy and probably noisy.

Students analyze and respond to literary and informational text.

Name ______________________________

Writing

Gather Information from Print and Digital Sources Gather information from print and digital sources about the two pets you chose, and write down your opinion about which pet you think is the best to own. Then make a list of your sources.

Responses will vary but should include a list of the student's print and digital sources, as well as a statement of the student's opinion on which pet he or she thinks is the best to own.

Conventions

Form Possessives

DIRECTIONS For each sentence, fill in the blank with the correct possessive form of the noun.

1. Babe was **Paul's** (Paul) ox.
2. The cookhouse **boys'** (boys) roller skates helped them move quickly.
3. My class agreed with **Charles's** (Charles) opinion about the story *Paul Bunyan*.

Students write routinely for a range of tasks, purposes, and audiences. Students practice various conventions of standard English.

Benchmark Vocabulary

Name ______________________________

DIRECTIONS Write a sentence using the word.

huddled

Responses should show contextual understanding of the word.

Write in Response to Reading

Read pages 32–35. Write an explanatory response about how the exaggerations help convey the central message. Use evidence from the text.

Responses should use evidence from the text, including that the exaggerations, such as "the flames froze solid," show how cold and difficult that winter was and how tough the pioneers were to overcome the hardships.

Students demonstrate contextual understanding of Benchmark Vocabulary. Students read text closely and use text evidence in their written answers.

Name ______________________________

Taking Shelter

The first week of May in Tornado Alley was active that year. Nearly every day after school, Kirsten heard the tornado siren from the nearby Oklahoma town. She rushed to her basement for shelter.

Kirsten's friend Julia had never spent tornado season in the area. She was staying with Kirsten because her parents were out of town. As the girls talked in the yard, the tornado siren wailed. Kirsten bolted toward her house. Julia asked Kirsten what she was doing. "Going to the basement!"

Julia stared at Kirsten as if she were crazy and foolish. She said that she and her parents never did anything when they heard a siren. Just then, Kirsten saw her mom frantically waving from the porch. "Come in, girls!"

In the basement, Kirsten told her mom what Julia had said. Kirsten's mom looked at Julia. "Let me tell you just how important tornado sirens are. This house is not the same one we bought. A tornado smashed the first one."

Julia's heart raced. Kirsten's mom explained, "That tornado had winds of up to 165 miles per hour. It was given an EF-3 rating on the Fujita (foo-JEE-ta) Scale. Do you know what the Fujita Scale is?" Julia nodded.

Kirsten's mom described the sound that the tornado made. "It was like a freight train speeding by," she said. Julia turned pale. She missed her parents and promised Kirsten's mom that she and her parents would take her advice. They would take shelter when the siren sounded.

Students read text closely to determine what the text says.

Sleuth Work

Name ______________________

Gather Evidence What traits would you use to describe each character in the story? Underline examples from the text to support your choices.

See annotations on previous page. Responses may vary but should show evidence from the text.

Gather Evidence: Extend Your Ideas Look at the traits you used to describe each character in the story. Make up a character and write 3–4 sentences describing him or her.

Responses will vary.

Ask Questions Write two questions you would ask a tornado expert. Underline twice details in the text that support your questions.

Responses may vary but might include, "How do you measure tornadoes?" "What does a tornado sound like?" "Why should you pay attention to tornado sirens?"

Ask Questions: Extend Your Ideas Do you have questions about tornadoes that aren't answered in the text? Where could you find their answers?

Questions may vary but students could find answers in books about tornadoes and on the Internet.

Make Your Case What do you think was the most convincing information that was shared with Julia to get her to promise to take cover next time? Circle it in the text, and write a sentence explaining your choice on a separate sheet of paper.

Responses may vary.

Make Your Case: Extend Your Ideas On a separate piece of paper, write a persuasive paragraph about a topic you introduce to a character. What convincing information did you include? **Responses will vary.**

Students read text closely to determine what the text says.

Writing

Name ____________________

Take Brief Notes on Sources Use your own words to take notes on the sources you found in Lesson 12. Your notes should describe facts and details that support your opinion (on which animal makes a better pet), as well as your reasons for this opinion. Organize your notes into categories. Write your notes on the lines below or on a separate sheet of paper.

Responses will vary but should include facts and details that support the student's opinion and the student's reasons for holding this opinion. The student's notes on his or her sources should be organized into categories.

Conventions

Use Possessives

DIRECTIONS Make the sentences easier to follow by using a possessive noun to show ownership.

1. The shovels of the lumberjacks were worn down from shoveling snow. **The lumberjacks' shovels were worn down from shoveling snow.**

2. The tunnels dug by the lumberjacks were deep under the snow. **The lumberjacks' tunnels were deep under the snow.**

3. The flames of the fire did not feel warm. **The fire's flames did not feel warm.**

Students write routinely for a range of tasks, purposes, and audiences. Students practice various conventions of standard English.

Benchmark Vocabulary

Name ______________________________

DIRECTIONS Write a sentence using each word.

eager groove boulders

Responses should show contextual understanding of the word.

Write in Response to Reading

Read the description of how the Grand Canyon was formed on page 39. Write an interview with Paul Bunyan that gives his explanation of the process for creating the canyon and how he felt about it. Use details from the text in your interview.

Responses should use evidence from the text, including that Paul was walking through the desert and dragging his great ax. The ax cut into the soft sand to create the Grand Canyon.

Students demonstrate contextual understanding of Benchmark Vocabulary. Students read text closely and use text evidence in their written answers.

Name ______________________

Determine the Central Message

DIRECTIONS Using evidence from the text, answer the following questions about pages 38–41 from *Paul Bunyan.*

1. How was the Mississippi River created?

   Paul hitched a plow to Babe, and they dug the river bed.

2. What caused Paul to accidentally create the Grand Canyon?

   It was very hot outside, and Paul was tired, so he dragged his ax behind him. The ax dug the canyon.

3. Why was Paul careful not to leave any footprints when he and Babe went out West?

   Paul didn't want to be found, but he was so big that he knew his footprints would be easy to follow, so he didn't leave any behind.

4. What is the central message of the story? How do these events help develop the story's central message?

   The central message is that Paul and Babe are like superheroes. Paul and Babe's creation of the Mississippi River and their creation of the Grand Canyon emphasize this central message because no human could do either of those things.

Students analyze and respond to literary and informational text.

Name ____________________

Plan and Prewrite Form an opinion about whether Paul is likeable, and think of reasons for your opinion. Take notes on details from the story that support your reasons. Then, on a separate sheet of paper, use this information to create an outline for an opinion essay.

Responses will vary but should include notes and an outline that include the student's opinion about Paul's likeability, reasons for his or her opinion, and details from the story that support his or her reasons.

Conventional Spelling for Suffixes

DIRECTIONS Read pages 38–41 of *Paul Bunyan*. Then list words from those pages that include the types of suffixes identified below.

1. List two words with a suffix that describes a past action.

   Possible responses: hitched, rushed, called, piled, walked, turned, liked, decided, needed, headed, ended

2. List two adjectives with a suffix that turns it into an adverb.

   Possible responses: neatly, terribly, deeply

3. List two words with a suffix that describes an action that is happening now.

   Possible responses: being, dragging, cutting, rushing

Students write routinely for a range of tasks, purposes, and audiences. Students practice various conventions of standard English.

Benchmark Vocabulary

Name ____

DIRECTIONS Write a sentence using each word.

stubborn eager

Responses should show contextual understanding of the word.

Write in Response to Reading

Read "Growing Up" and "Moving On" in *Paul Bunyan*. Do you think Paul would have chosen to be a regular-sized person if he had had a choice? Support your response with evidence from the text.

Responses should use evidence from the text.

Students demonstrate contextual understanding of Benchmark Vocabulary. Students read text closely and use text evidence in their written answers.

Writing

Name ______________________________

Draft an Opinion Essay Use the outline you wrote in Lesson 14 to write a draft of your opinion essay. Your essay should include your opinion, reasons for that opinion, and evidence from the text that supports your reasons. Write your draft on a separate sheet of paper.

Responses will vary but should include a draft of the student's opinion essay that presents his or her opinion, reasons for that opinion, and evidence from the text that supports those reasons.

Conventions

Adjust Spellings for Endings

DIRECTIONS Read each sentence carefully. On the line next to the sentence, write *correct* if the underlined word is spelled correctly. If it is not, write the correct spelling on the line.

1. That winter was the <u>coldest</u> yet. **correct**
2. Paul's tennis shoes are <u>weter</u> than Amy's boots. **wetter**
3. When Paul was a baby, his <u>crys</u> broke the windows. **cries**

Students write routinely for a range of tasks, purposes, and audiences. Students practice various conventions of standard English.

Name ______________________________

Suffixes *-er, -or, -ess, -ist*

DIRECTIONS Add the suffix to each base word. Write the new word on the line.

1. edit + -or = editor

2. art + -ist = artist

3. conduct + -or = conductor

4. sell + -er = seller

5. lion + -ess = lioness

DIRECTIONS Write the word from the Word Bank that best fits each definition.

Word Bank

shipper	governess	biologist	diarist	investigator

diarist **6.** a person who keeps a diary

shipper **7.** one who ships packages

investigator **8.** one who investigates

biologist **9.** a scientist in the field of biology

governess **10.** in past centuries, a woman who taught children

DIRECTIONS Add the suffix ***-er, -or, -ess,*** or ***-ist*** to the base word in parentheses to complete each sentence. Write the word on the line.

swimmer **11.** Gertrude Ederle was the first woman (swim) to successfully cross the English Channel.

medalist **12.** Before the crossing, she had been a gold (medal) in the 1924 Olympics.

competitor **13.** She was quite a (competition), and held 29 U.S. and world records.

actress **14.** Unlike Olympic skater Sonja Henie, Ederle did not become an (act).

instructor **15.** Instead, Ederle had a career as a swimming (instruct) for children with hearing difficulties.

Students apply grade-level phonics and word analysis skills.

Benchmark Vocabulary

Name ______________________

DIRECTIONS Write a sentence using each word.

ashamed huddled

Responses should show contextual understanding of the word.

Write in Response to Reading

Read page 38 in *Paul Bunyan*. Do you believe the explanations for how the Rocky Mountains and Mississippi River were created? Then read pages 18–28 in *Storm in the Night*. Do you believe Grandfather's story? Explain why you do or do not believe the events from each story using evidence from the texts.

Responses may vary but should include that the stories in Paul Bunyan are tall tales about the creation of the Rocky Mountains and the Mississippi River. Grandfather's story is more believable; it is possible that a dog gets out in a storm and that the dog's owner has to find him.

Students demonstrate contextual understanding of Benchmark Vocabulary. Students read text closely and use text evidence in their written answers.

Name ______________________

Writing

Revise a Draft Revise the opinion essay you drafted in Lesson 15. Look for ways to use a more interesting word, avoid repeating the same words or phrases, add linking words and phrases, add or clarify details to explain reasons, and add or strengthen the concluding statement. Write your revised essay on a separate sheet of paper.

Responses will vary but should include a revision of the student's opinion essay that includes better word choice, fewer repeated words and phrases, linking words and phrases, clear supporting details, and a strong concluding statement.

Conventions

Conventional Spelling for High-Frequency Words

DIRECTIONS For each word, write *correct* if the word is spelled correctly or *incorrect* if the word is spelled incorrectly. Then write a sentence with the word, using its correct spelling.

1. thaught **incorrect**

   I thought that the essay was interesting.

2. becawse **incorrect**

   I like this song because I can dance to it.

3. favorite **correct**

   This is my favorite story.

Students write routinely for a range of tasks, purposes, and audiences. Students practice various conventions of standard English.

Benchmark Vocabulary

Name ______________________________

DIRECTIONS Write a sentence using each word.

banished secure ecstatic managed

Responses should show contextual understanding of the word.

Write in Response to Reading

What central message do "The Myth of Icarus" and "Anansi's Long, Thin Legs: An African Fable" share? How is this message developed in both texts? Use evidence from both texts in your response. Write your answer below or on a separate sheet of paper.

Responses will vary but could include that both share the central message that greed is dangerous. Anansi was greedy and wanted food from eight animals, so he tied his legs to eight different pots. This caused his legs to be stretched out. Icarus was greedy because he wanted to fly higher and higher, so the wax on his wings melted, and he fell into the ocean and died.

Students demonstrate contextual understanding of Benchmark Vocabulary. Students read text closely and use text evidence in their written answers.

Name ______________________

Writing

Edit an Essay On a separate sheet of paper, edit the opinion essay you developed in Lessons 14–16. Correct any errors in grammar, capitalization, spelling, and punctuation. Then make sure that your essay has all of its parts.

Responses will vary but should include an edited opinion essay with correct grammar, capitalization, spelling, and punctuation.

Conventions

Consult a Dictionary to Check and Correct Spellings

DIRECTIONS Use a print or digital dictionary to check the spelling of each word below. If the word is spelled correctly, write *correct* on the line next to the word. If the word is spelled incorrectly, write the correct spelling on the line next to the word.

1. desparate **desperate**
2. consert **concert**
3. triumphant **correct**

Students write routinely for a range of tasks, purposes, and audiences. Students practice various conventions of standard English.

Benchmark Vocabulary

Name ______________________________

DIRECTIONS Write a sentence using each word.

hitched comfortable surround mutterings

Responses should show contextual understanding of the word.

Write in Response to Reading

Read page 40 in *Paul Bunyan*, page 20 in *Knots on a Counting Rope*, and page 30 in *Storm in the Night*. On a separate sheet of paper, write a brief essay in which you describe how each text conveys its central message or lesson through key details. Use evidence from the text in your response.

Responses should use evidence from the text. In *Paul Bunyan,* the central message is that Paul's strength helped him created the landscape. This is a tall tale and includes exaggeration. In *Knots on a Counting Rope*, the central message is that strength is about overcoming obstacles. Grandfather keeps telling the boy the same story so he'll become stronger and stronger and can overcome his disability. The boy can still race horses, and he walks in beauty. In *Storm in the Night*, the central message is that it is normal to be afraid. Grandfather's story tells about being afraid but overcoming that fear to find his dog.

Students demonstrate contextual understanding of Benchmark Vocabulary. Students read text closely and use text evidence in their written answers.

Reading Analysis

Name ______________________________

Compare and Contrast

DIRECTIONS Using evidence from the texts, answer the following questions about *Knots on a Counting Rope*, *Storm in the Night*, and *Paul Bunyan*.

1. Which word or phrase could be used to describe the main characters in all three stories?

Responses will vary but could include the word *strong*.

2. How does this trait help each main character? Explain your answer using details from the stories.

Responses will vary but should include that Paul Bunyan was physically strong and could do many feats of strength. Grandfather's story in *Storm in the Night,* about being scared but still doing something scary, is also about strength and being able to overcome fear. Boy in *Knots on a Counting Rope* is strong because he has courage to "cross the dark mountains" even though he is blind.

3. After reading all three stories, what might readers learn about the importance of having this trait?

Responses may vary but could include that dealing with uncertainty and being willing to move forward can make people strong.

4. From reading all three stories, what do readers learn about the purpose of telling stories?

Responses may vary but could include that storytelling is a way people share messages and explain things in the world.

Students analyze and respond to literary and informational text.

Name ______________________________

Publish and Present Neatly write the final version of your opinion essay on a separate sheet of paper.

Responses will vary but should include a neatly written, final version of the student's opinion essay.

Capitalize Appropriate Words in Titles

DIRECTIONS Below are new titles for *Knots on a Counting Rope*, *Storm in the Night*, and *Paul Bunyan*. Rewrite the titles with correct capitalization.

1. the blue horses **The Blue Horses**
2. thomas, grandfather, and the big storm **Thomas, Grandfather, and the Big Storm**
3. the strongest lumberjack in the world **The Strongest Lumberjack in the World**

Students write routinely for a range of tasks, purposes, and audiences. Students practice various conventions of standard English.

Name ______________________________

Syllable Pattern VCCCV

DIRECTIONS Choose the word in parentheses with the VCCCV syllable pattern to finish each sentence. Write the word on the line.

children **1.** The (students/children) took a trip to the zoo.

surprise **2.** Their teachers arranged for a (surprise/selection).

address **3.** The zookeeper gave an (alert/address) to the group.

inspect **4.** She told them to (watch/inspect) each animal habitat.

contrast **5.** She said to (compare/contrast) the animals' homes.

hundreds **6.** That day, they saw (dozens/hundreds) of animals.

DIRECTIONS Circle the word that has the VCCCV syllable pattern. Then write a sentence on the line that uses the word you circled.

7. forgive monster wonder

____

8. human fortress winner

____

9. complain number writer

____

10. constant planet signal

____

11. beyond robin sample

____

12. chosen 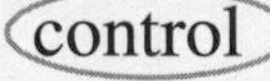 control copper

____

Students apply grade-level phonics and word analysis skills.

Benchmark Vocabulary

Name ______________________________

DIRECTIONS Write a sentence using each word.

atmosphere extends intense equator exchange

Responses should show contextual understanding of the word.

Write in Response to Reading

Read page 6 of *Weather.* Write a paragraph in which you discuss the relationship between insolation and the greenhouse effect, using text evidence to support your writing.

Responses should use evidence from the text, including that insolation is when two-thirds of the heat from the sun is absorbed by the atmosphere. This heat warms the ground and the air near the surface. Because of the greenhouse effect, the atmosphere doesn't allow most of the heat to escape back into space. Because of insolation and the greenhouse effect, our planet is livable.

Students demonstrate contextual understanding of Benchmark Vocabulary. Students read text closely and use text evidence in their written answers.

Writing

Name ______________________________

Convey Ideas and Information Think about the different types of weather you experience in your area during each season. Using a Four-Column Chart, with each of the seasons listed as headings, write down words that describe each season. Then think about whether today is a typical day for the season and whether it matches any of the words in your chart. Below, write a few sentences about today's weather and whether today is a seasonal day.

Responses will vary but should include more than one sentence containing specific details describing today's weather and a statement as to whether it is a seasonal day.

Conventions

Functions of Adverbs in Sentences

DIRECTIONS Circle the adverb in each sentence. Then write the word that the adverb modifies and whether it is a verb, an adjective, or another adverb.

1. A (remarkably) large thundercloud appeared in the distance.
   large, adjective
2. The soft breeze blew (gently) through the trees. **blew, verb**
3. Our journey began (unusually) early in the morning.
   early, adverb

Students write routinely for a range of tasks, purposes, and audiences. Students practice various conventions of standard English.

Name ______________________________

DIRECTIONS Write a sentence using each word.

rotation currents altitude continuous advances

Responses should show contextual understanding of the word.

Read the first sentence on page 10 of *Weather*. Write an opinion paragraph stating whether or not you agree that weather-related issues are not simple. Use text evidence to support your writing.

Responses should use evidence from the text.

Students demonstrate contextual understanding of Benchmark Vocabulary. Students read text closely and use text evidence in their written answers.

Name ______________________________

Scientific Ideas

DIRECTIONS Using evidence from the text, answer the following questions about pages 10–15 from *Weather*.

1. What effect does the difference in the speeds of rotation at Earth's equator and near the poles have on winds and ocean currents?

   The difference in the speeds of rotation causes winds and ocean currents to curve to their right in the Northern Hemisphere and to their left in the Southern Hemisphere.

2. How much of the sun's energy is absorbed by forests and trees? How much of the sun's energy is reflected by a fresh snowfall?

   Forests and trees absorb most of the sun's energy. A fresh snowfall reflects as much as nine tenths of the sun's energy.

3. What is a *front?* What is the difference between a cold front and a warm front?

   A front is the boundary line between cold and warm air masses. A cold front is when a cold air mass advances as a warm air mass retreats. A warm front is when a warm air mass advances as a cold air mass retreats.

Students analyze and respond to literary and informational text.

Name ______________________________

Understand and Identify Genre Choose a U.S. city to research. Use the weather site your teacher assigned to research today's weather and tomorrow's forecast for your chosen city. Take notes on your research. Then identify the genre of informative writing that you would produce from these notes, and briefly explain why you chose this genre.

Responses will vary but should include the current weather and next-day forecast for a U.S. city from the assigned online weather site, the genre of either report writing or explanatory writing, and a brief but accurate explanation of the choice.

Review of Adverbs in Sentences

DIRECTIONS Underline the adverb in each sentence. Then write the verb the adverb modifies and whether the adverb describes *how, when,* or *where* the action takes place.

1. We left town yesterday around noon. **left, when**
2. I dashed upstairs to grab my umbrella. **dashed, where**
3. She threw her books carelessly on the table. **threw, how**

Students write routinely for a range of tasks, purposes, and audiences. Students practice various conventions of standard English.

Name ________________________

Benchmark Vocabulary

DIRECTIONS Write a sentence using each word.

properties unstable unsettled

Responses should show contextual understanding of the word.

Write in Response to Reading

Read pages 16–21 of *Weather*. Select one type of cloud, and write a paragraph about it. Use text evidence to support your writing.

Responses should use evidence from the text. Cumulus clouds are low-level, only a few hundred yards thick, and separated by clear sky. They form on sunny days. Stratus clouds are low-lying and have broad and thin layers. If clouds are thick enough, "rain may fall." Sun "burns off" the clouds. Cirrus clouds are high-level clouds, formed of ice crystals. They often form before a warm front comes through.

Students demonstrate contextual understanding of Benchmark Vocabulary. Students read text closely and use text evidence in their written answers.

Name ______________________________

Weather Work

Do you need a jacket today? Will you need an umbrella? Meteorologists help us answer those kinds of weather questions. Meteorologists are more than just the people on TV telling us what the weather is going to be like today. Meteorologists are scientists. They go to school to learn all about the weather and what creates it.

Predicting the weather is a big part of being a meteorologist. Today, meteorologists depend on technology and weather observers around the world to help them.

Weather observers are very important to meteorologists. These observers make measurements every day at nearly 10,000 different weather stations. Thousands of ships at sea record the weather also. More than 500 weather stations release weather balloons. The balloons collect weather data. All of this data is closely examined. Then the data is used to make weather predictions.

Being a meteorologist is an important job! Meteorologists help us stay safe during dangerous weather. They work with city managers to plan the number of snowplows needed during winter storms. They provide information to power companies. This helps the companies meet energy needs during hot or cold spells. They even help sporting event organizers predict whether a game can go on after a rain delay.

The next time you watch a meteorologist on TV, keep in mind that the two-minute weather forecast is based on hours of research. Three cheers for meteorologists!

Students read text closely to determine what the text says.

Name ______________________________

Gather Evidence Circle the clues in "Weather Work" that tell you the writer's opinion about meteorologists. **See annotations on previous page.**

Gather Evidence: Extend Your Ideas Do you agree or disagree with the writer? Write three sentences stating your opinion using text evidence.

Responses will vary but should use text evidence.

____

____

Ask Questions Underline information from the text that you have questions about. **Responses may vary.**

Ask Questions: Extend Your Ideas Write down two questions you have about meteorologists after reading "Weather Work."

Responses may vary.

____

____

Make Your Case How did the writer group information in the selection? Draw a box around one or two words or phrases that you think best describe the information in each paragraph. **Responses may vary but could include annotations on previous page.**

Make Your Case: Extend Your Ideas Look at the words you boxed. Underline twice supporting details you found in the paragraphs.

Responses may vary.

Students read text closely to determine what the text says.

Name ______________________________

Choose Details Use key details to determine the main idea of pages 16–21 of *Weather*. Then use examples to show how the main idea is supported in the text. Write a paragraph explaining how the author used key details to support the main idea of the text to inform readers about the topic.

Responses will vary but should include a statement of the main idea of pp. 16–21 of *Weather*, relevant supporting examples, and an explanation of how key details support the main idea to inform readers about the topic.

Use of Comparative Adverbs

DIRECTIONS Read each sentence and look at the adverb in parentheses. Rewrite the sentence to include the comparative form of the adverb.

1. The clouds moved (fast) across the sky than they did before.
   The clouds moved faster across the sky than they did before.

2. The sun rose a little (early) today than it did yesterday.
   The sun rose a little earlier today than it did yesterday.

3. The rain came down (gently) than it did this morning.
   The rain came down more gently than it did this morning.

Students write routinely for a range of tasks, purposes, and audiences. Students practice various conventions of standard English.

Benchmark Vocabulary

Name ______________________________

DIRECTIONS Write a sentence using each word.

condensed resistance evaporates

Responses should show contextual understanding of the word.

Write in Response to Reading

Skim pages 22–27 of *Weather*, and then write an opinion paragraph about the photographs on those pages. Do the photographs add to the text? Are different photographs needed? Support your writing by using text evidence.

Responses should use evidence from the text.

Students demonstrate contextual understanding of Benchmark Vocabulary. Students read text closely and use text evidence in their written answers.

Name ______________________________

Information from Illustrations

DIRECTIONS Using evidence from the text, answer the following questions about pages 22–27 from *Weather*.

1. How do the text on page 22 and the photograph on page 23 work together to help the reader understand the concept of precipitation?

   Responses may vary but could include that the text describes different forms of precipitation, and the photograph shows one particular form of precipitation.

2. How do the photographs on page 24 support the text information on this page?

   Responses may vary but could include that the photographs show the complex six-sided shape of snowflakes that is described in the second paragraph.

3. What does the photograph on page 25 show? What information does this image provide that is not provided in the text?

   The photograph on page 25 shows a large hailstone. Reponses may vary but could include that the photograph shows the different colors of the crystals in a hailstone, which the text does not mention.

4. What text detail about frost does the photograph on page 27 illustrate?

   Responses may vary but could include that the photograph on page 27 illustrates the detail that frost inside windowpanes has a feathery appearance.

Students analyze and respond to literary and informational text.

Name ______________________

Writing

Introduce the Topic Choose a weather-related topic, and use a Main Idea graphic organizer to plan the main idea and key details you will write about. Below, write the sentences that will introduce the topic, including a sentence that will grab the reader's interest and attention.

Responses will vary but should include a few introductory sentences for a weather-related topic, including a sentence that will grab the reader's interest and attention.

Conventions

Use Superlative Adverbs

DIRECTIONS Complete each sentence with the superlative form of the verb in parentheses.

1. My two friends and I ran home to escape the hail, and I ran **farthest** (far).
2. A brief rainstorm has hit the area each day for the past three days, but today's rainstorm hit **hardest** (hard).
3. Of all the weather predictions the meteorologist has made this week, she predicted today's weather **most accurately** (accurately).

Students write routinely for a range of tasks, purposes, and audiences. Students practice various conventions of standard English.

Benchmark Vocabulary

Name ______________________________

DIRECTIONS Write a sentence using each word.

conditions reduce irritate

Responses should show contextual understanding of the word.

Write in Response to Reading

Read the first two paragraphs on page 30 of *Weather*. Write a paragraph that explains the scientific ideas that lead to the creation of smog pollution, using text evidence to support your writing.

Responses should use evidence from the text, including that burning coal and oil leads to gray smog. Also, brown smog is caused mainly by the fumes of cars. It "can reduce visibility and irritate eyes, throat, and lungs. And both gray and brown smog can damage metal, rubber, and other materials."

Students demonstrate contextual understanding of Benchmark Vocabulary. Students read text closely and use text evidence in their written answers.

Name ______________________________

Writing

Develop a Topic Use the graphic organizer you created in Lesson 4 to develop your topic with facts, definitions, and details for an informational news report. Identify facts, definitions, and details to develop your topic, and then write a news report that is one or two paragraphs long. Use the lines below or a separate sheet of paper.

Responses will vary but should include a weather-related topic that is developed with relevant facts, definitions, and details in the form of a one- to two-paragraph news report.

Conventions

Select Comparative or Superlative Adverbs

DIRECTIONS Circle the comparative or superlative adverb that correctly completes each sentence.

1. Today it's snowing much (harder / hardest) than it was last week.
2. Of all the local teens who shovel snow, Janine shovels the (more carefully / most carefully).
3. The blizzard arrived much (earlier / earliest) than the meteorologist predicted.

Students write routinely for a range of tasks, purposes, and audiences. Students practice various conventions of standard English.

Name ______________________________

Syllable Pattern CV/VC

DIRECTIONS Circle the word with two vowels together where each vowel has a separate vowel sound. Then draw a line between the letters that stand for the separate sounds.

1. clean	plain	radios	radi|os
2. audience	faith	search	audi|ence
3. either	medium	southern	medi|um
4. beach	pound	pioneer	pi|oneer
5. greed	journal	ideas	ide|as
6. reality	poison	waiter	re|ality
7. stadium	grain	group	stadi|um
8. freeze	create	stream	cre|ate

DIRECTIONS Read the paragraph. Words with two vowels together are underlined. Circle the underlined words in which the two vowels have separate sounds. The vowels may or may not be followed by a consonant. Write the words on the lines.

Maria wants to know the reasons for different musical sounds. Her mother is a violinist and her father is a pianist. Both instruments have strings that can be plucked or hit. Would a plucked violin string sound like a hit piano string? To find out, she created a duet for her parents. They played it in a giant recording studio. The results influenced Maria's scientific study of music.

9. Maria	**13.** piano	**17.** studio
10. violinist	**14.** created	**18.** influenced
11. pianist	**15.** duet	**19.** Maria's
12. violin	**16.** giant	**20.** scientific

Students apply grade-level phonics and word analysis skills.

Name ______________________________

Benchmark Vocabulary

DIRECTIONS Write a sentence using each word.

atmosphere intense absorbed

Responses should show contextual understanding of the word.

Write in Response to Reading

Look at the photograph on page 31 of *Weather*. Describe the photograph. How is the picture related to the text? Does it help you better understand the text? Why or why not?

Responses should use evidence from the text, including that the smoke from the smokestacks of the city are creating a cumulus cloud. This shows what the text is explaining. Student opinions may vary.

Students demonstrate contextual understanding of Benchmark Vocabulary. Students read text closely and use text evidence in their written answers.

Writing

Name ______________________________

Group Related Information Group related information for the topic of your news report, organize the information into categories using a Web B graphic organizer, and use this information in your news report.

Responses will vary but should include related information grouped together and organized into appropriate categories for a news report.

Conventions

Select Comparative or Superlative Adverbs

DIRECTIONS Read the sentences in items 1–3. Combine the sentences in each item into an original sentence using the comparative or superlative form of the adverb in parentheses. Write the new sentence on the line.

1. The ice in the sun melts. The ice in the shade melts. (fast)

Sample response: The ice in the sun melts faster than the ice in the shade does.

2. Earth rotates at the equator. Earth rotates at the poles. (rapidly)

Sample response: Earth rotates more rapidly at the equator than it does at the poles.

3. I skied one mile. She skied two miles. He skied three miles. (far)

Sample response: I skied one mile, and she skied two miles, but he skied the farthest—three miles.

Students write routinely for a range of tasks, purposes, and audiences. Students practice various conventions of standard English.

Benchmark Vocabulary

Name ______________________________

DIRECTIONS Write a sentence using each word.

properties unstable unsettled

Responses should show contextual understanding of the word.

Write in Response to Reading

Read page 18 of *Weather*. Write a paragraph that explains the difference between literal and nonliteral uses of words and phrases, using text evidence to support your writing.

Responses should use evidence from the text, including that describing the clouds as "puffy, dome-shaped balls of cotton" is an example of nonliteral language. The rest of the page is literal and deals with the specifics of the clouds ("less than a mile above Earth," "a few hundred yards thick," etc.).

Students demonstrate contextual understanding of Benchmark Vocabulary. Students read text closely and use text evidence in their written answers.

Name ______________________________

Literal and Nonliteral Meanings

DIRECTIONS Using evidence from the text, answer the following questions about *Weather*.

1. Read the first sentence of the second paragraph on page 4. Explain the nonliteral meaning of the word *ocean* in this sentence. Then state its literal meaning.

The word *ocean* describes the large amount of air that surrounds Earth. The literal meaning of *ocean* is "one of the large bodies of salt water found on Earth."

2. In the second paragraph on page 10, the author uses the word *colorful* to describe the names of regional winds. What are the literal and nonliteral meanings of *colorful*?

Literal meaning: "having many different colors"; nonliteral meaning: "interesting"

3. Read the third paragraph on page 16. Does the word *families* in the first sentence have a literal or nonliteral meaning? Explain.

The word *families* has a nonliteral meaning because it does not refer people who are related to one another, but instead refers to categories of clouds.

4. Read the first paragraph on page 30. Is the meaning of the word *troubled* in the last sentence literal or nonliteral? Explain.

The meaning of *troubled* is nonliteral because it describes how cities are affected by smog rather than describing a person who is worried about something.

Students analyze and respond to literary and informational text.

Writing

Name ______________________________

Use Illustrations Create an illustration for your news report. The illustration should provide additional facts, definitions, or details that support the main idea of your news report. You may need to include a caption or a label to help readers understand the main idea and details of the illustration. Use the space below to write notes about your illustration.

Responses will vary but should include notes on an illustration that will provide additional information to support the main idea of the student's weather-related news report, including notes on any clarifying caption or label.

Conventions

Define Abstract Nouns

DIRECTIONS Circle the abstract noun in each sentence. Then write whether each noun names a feeling or a quality.

1. Curiosity is important if you want to become a scientist.
   quality
2. The meteorologist's dedication to her work was admirable.
   quality
3. I shared his delight at the news that the rain would stop by midday.
   feeling

Students write routinely for a range of tasks, purposes, and audiences. Students practice various conventions of standard English.

Benchmark Vocabulary

Name ______________________________

DIRECTIONS Write a sentence using each word.

hoist axis orbits humid

Responses should show contextual understanding of the word.

Write in Response to Reading

Read page 54 in the *Text Collection*. The words *wide* and *dry* are used to describe a plain in the text. These words can be used to describe many things in real life, such as a classroom board (wide) and unused paper towels (dry). What else can you use these words to describe? Support your answers with evidence from the text.

Responses may vary but could include that the sky is wide, as the illustration shows.

Students demonstrate contextual understanding of Benchmark Vocabulary. Students read text closely and use text evidence in their written answers.

Writing

Name ______________________________

Connect Ideas Within Categories Add linking words and phrases to your news report. Identify linking words and phrases that connect similar ideas and those that connect contrasting ideas. Then use them to connect events in your news report. Write your revised report on the lines below or on a separate sheet of paper.

Responses will vary but should include a revised news report that features comparing and contrasting linking words and phases used correctly to connect events or actions.

Conventions

Use Abstract Nouns

DIRECTIONS Circle the abstract noun in each sentence. On the line, write an original sentence that contains the abstract noun you circled.

1. The beauty of the winter landscape inspired me to take a photograph.
   The rainbow's beauty was striking.

2. Her determination to pursue a career as a meteorologist was inspiring.
   His determination helped him win the game.

3. He showed great courage when navigating the ship through rough waters.
   I admired their courage in facing the problem.

Students write routinely for a range of tasks, purposes, and audiences. Students practice various conventions of standard English.

Benchmark Vocabulary

Name ______________________________

DIRECTIONS Write a sentence using each word.

hoist axis

Responses should show contextual understanding of the word.

Write in Response to Reading

Read pages 56–57 of the *Text Collection*. Write a paragraph stating your opinion about how the author describes weather and its causes around the world. Use evidence from the text to support your answers.

Opinions may vary but students should use text evidence to support them, including that as the Earth orbits the sun, the tilt of its axis determines the seasons. If the North Pole is tilted toward the sun, it is summer in the northern hemisphere. If the South Pole is tilted toward the sun, it is summer in the southern hemisphere. When either pole is tilted away from the sun, its hemisphere is in winter. Also, there are places where the weather doesn't change much, such as in the equatorial rain forests.

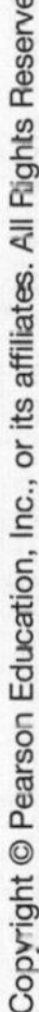

Students demonstrate contextual understanding of Benchmark Vocabulary. Students read text closely and use text evidence in their written answers.

Name ______________________________

Scientific Ideas

DIRECTIONS Using evidence from the text, answer the following questions about pages 45–56 of the *Text Collection*.

1. Read page 45. What happens to the snow fort in Alberta, Canada? What causes this event to happen?

   The snow fort melts. This event is caused by a wind called the chinook.

2. Read page 52. What happens when the rains come to Northern Kenya? What effect does this have on the people's actions? What effect does the author suggest will happen when the sun shines?

   Rains come to Northern Kenya, a river forms and people hurry to drink the water and play. The author suggests that when the sun shines, the river will quickly dry up.

3. Read the second paragraph on page 56. What happens to the North Pole and the South Pole in March? What effect does this have on the Arctic and Antarctica?

   In March, the North Pole tilts toward the sun and the South Pole tilts away from the sun. The effect of this is that the Arctic gets six months of daylight and warmer weather, while Antarctica gets six months of darkness and bitter cold.

Students analyze and respond to literary and informational text.

Name ____________________

Provide a Concluding Statement Write a concluding statement for your news report. First, review your writing for details that support your main idea. Then ask yourself why you chose the topic or what you found the most interesting about it. Use this information to help you come up with a concluding statement that summarizes your report, gives the reader something to think about, or wraps up the information in an interesting way.

Responses will vary but should include a concluding statement that features relevant supporting details from the student's news report to summarize the report, give the reader something to think about, or wrap up the information in an interesting way.

Form the Past Tense of Irregular Verbs

DIRECTIONS Circle the present-tense verb in each sentence. Then identify the correct past-tense form of the verb. On the line, rewrite the sentence with the past-tense verb.

1. I (drive) slowly and carefully through the snowstorm.
   I drove slowly and carefully through the snowstorm.

2. Due to the falling temperature, the water (freeze).
   Due to the falling temperature, the water froze.

3. Many difficulties (arise) because of the icy streets.
   Many difficulties arose because of the icy streets.

Students write routinely for a range of tasks, purposes, and audiences. Students practice various conventions of standard English.

Benchmark Vocabulary

Name ______________________________

DIRECTIONS Write a sentence using each word.

conditions reduce irritate humid

Responses should show contextual understanding of the word.

Write in Response to Reading

Read page 50 of the *Text Collection* and page 16 of *Weather*. In your opinion, which text does a better job of expressing its key details? Use specific examples from the texts to support your answer.

Opinions may vary but students should use text evidence to support them, including that on page 50 of *On the Same Day in March,* the description of hail is figurative and descriptive but the book doesn't explain how hail happens. The information about clouds in *Weather* is scientific and more detailed.

Students demonstrate contextual understanding of Benchmark Vocabulary. Students read text closely and use text evidence in their written answers.

Name ______________________

Provide a Concluding Section Review the writing work that you completed in Lessons 4–9. Create a concluding section for your news report on the lines below. Then write the final version of your news report on a separate sheet of paper.

Responses will vary but should include a concluding section for the student's news report and a final version of the report that includes this concluding section.

Use the Past Tense of Irregular Verbs

DIRECTIONS Circle the past-tense verb that correctly completes each sentence. Then use the past-tense verb in an original sentence. Write the new sentence on the line.

1. The storm (becomed / became) so severe that we stayed home.
   The day became sunny, so we went outside.

2. The lightning bolt hit the tree branch and (broke / breaked) it.
   My umbrella broke when the wind turned it inside out.

3. They went outside and (maked / made) a snowman after the blizzard.
   Dad made them hot chocolate after they came inside.

Students write routinely for a range of tasks, purposes, and audiences. Students practice various conventions of standard English.

Name ______________________________

Homophones

DIRECTIONS Choose the word that best matches each definition. Write the word on the line.

cell	**1.** a small room in a prison	sell	cell
write	**2.** to record on paper	write	right
hour	**3.** 60 minutes	hour	our
weak	**4.** not strong	week	weak
night	**5.** a period of darkness	night	knight
ate	**6.** swallowed	eight	ate
tale	**7.** a story	tail	tale
too	**8.** also	to	too

DIRECTIONS Choose the word that best matches each definition. Write the word on the line.

sent **9.** My aunt (cent/sent) us a text.

hear **10.** We couldn't (hear/here) each other on the phone.

meet **11.** Her text said she would (meet/meat) us outside.

plane **12.** Our (plain/plane) arrived late, though.

see **13.** We looked everywhere and could not (sea/see) her.

I **14.** Finally, (eye/I) spotted her bright green van.

knew **15.** Then I (new/knew) we would be fine.

Students apply grade-level phonics and word analysis skills.

Name ______________________

Benchmark Vocabulary

DIRECTIONS Write a sentence using each word.

predictable damage preparations evacuate devastated

Responses should show contextual understanding of the word.

Write in Response to Reading

Read page 12 of *Living Through a Natural Disaster.* Write a paragraph to explain some measures the city of Darwin has taken to be prepared for another cyclone. Use evidence from the text to support your answer.

Responses should use evidence from the text, including that new buildings were built to "withstand the force of a cyclone." "Public cyclone shelters were also built."

Students demonstrate contextual understanding of Benchmark Vocabulary. Students read text closely and use text evidence in their written answers.

Writing

Name ______________________________

Recall Information from Experiences Complete the Web A graphic organizer to recall information about a significant weather event you have experienced in your lifetime. Then write the details in the space below.

Responses will vary but should include specific details about a significant weather event that the student experienced.

Conventions

Function of Past-Tense Verbs

DIRECTIONS Use the past-tense form of the verb in parentheses to complete each sentence.

1. During last night's storm, I **accepted** (accept) his offer of an umbrella.
2. She **cleaned** (clean) the floor after the dog ran through the kitchen with muddy paws.
3. The floor got muddy because the dog **disobeyed** (disobey) his owner's command to "Stay."

Students write routinely for a range of tasks, purposes, and audiences. Students practice various conventions of standard English.

Benchmark Vocabulary

Name ________________________________

DIRECTIONS Write a sentence using each word.

meanders nourishes erosion irrigation

Responses should show contextual understanding of the word.

Write in Response to Reading

Read page 20 of *Living Through a Natural Disaster.* Do you believe that people living near the Huang River are safer now than in years past? Use evidence from the text to support your answer.

Responses should use evidence from the text, including that "trees and other vegetation were planted along the river" to absorb rainfall and reduce soil erosion. Also the river's water level is very low.

Students demonstrate contextual understanding of Benchmark Vocabulary. Students read text closely and use text evidence in their written answers.

Reading Analysis

Name ______________________

Use Illustrations

DIRECTIONS Using evidence from the text, answer the following questions about pages 13–20 of *Living Through a Natural Disaster.*

1. Look at the diagram on page 16. What is the main cause of the water rising in the river?

   the silt on the riverbed

2. What should readers understand after viewing the diagram "How the Huang He Became So High"?

   They should know that the silt pushed the water up, so the dikes were built up to hold it in. The water level kept going up until the dikes collapsed.

3. How are the details in the text on pages 16–17 different from the information in the diagram?

   The text tells about what the people did to stop the water from overflowing and what happened as a result. The diagram explains how the water got so high.

4. Look at the photo on page 20 of the Huang He today. How do the photo and key details from the text help readers understand how the Huang He has changed in some areas?

   The text says "some parts of the Huang He are nearly dry." This is shown in the photo with the dry docks that used to be filled to the top with water and the boats sitting almost on land.

Students analyze and respond to literary and informational text.

Name ________________

Writing

Take Brief Notes and Quote from a Text Write a paragraph that answers a research question about the Huang He flood, using your notes from the text.

Responses will vary but should include the answer to a research question about the Huang He flood, based on the student's notes from the text.

Conventions

Function of Irregular Past-Tense Verbs

DIRECTIONS Circle the past-tense verb in each sentence. On the short line, write whether the circled past-tense verb is regular or irregular. Then use the circled verb in an original sentence. Write the new sentence on the long line.

1. I listened to the weather forecast this morning. regular

   They listened to the wind whistle through the trees.

2. The family swam in the ocean during the trip. irregular

   We swam in the river one hot summer day.

3. They built a dike to keep the river from overflowing. irregular

   The children built a snowman after the snowstorm.

Students write routinely for a range of tasks, purposes, and audiences. Students practice various conventions of standard English.

Name ________________________________

Benchmark Vocabulary

DIRECTIONS Write a sentence using each word.

affects diverse habitats consequences international

Responses should show contextual understanding of the word.

Write in Response to Reading

Read page 28 of *Living Through a Natural Disaster.* What are some ways the El Niño of 1997 has helped people plan and prepare for future disasters? Use evidence from the text in your answer.

Responses should use evidence from the text, including that "they created a plan to ensure that people would have food and water throughout the drought and to limit damage to livestock and crops."

Students demonstrate contextual understanding of Benchmark Vocabulary. Students read text closely and use text evidence in their written answers.

Name ______________________________

Be Prepared!

Are you ready for an emergency? In school, you prepare with practice drills in case of a fire, tornado, or hurricane. Do you practice being ready for an emergency at home?

You need to put together an emergency kit! This kit should always be kept in a place at home that is easy to remember and find. If disaster hits, the emergency kit should supply you with everything you need. You should be prepared to be without electricity or water for a couple of days.

One of the most important supplies in an emergency kit is water. You'll need one gallon of water per person in your family for at least three days. You should also have three days' worth of food. Food needs to be nonperishable. That means food that cannot spoil. Foods like granola bars, canned tuna, dried fruits, and crackers are some examples.

A radio that can be powered by batteries is also important. You'll need to know what is happening. Be sure to have extra batteries in your emergency supply kit too. Flashlights, a whistle to signal for help, and a first-aid kit are also very important.

Once you create your emergency supply kit, be sure to check your food and water supplies every six months. You may want to replace them then to have fresh food and water on hand.

During an emergency, always remember to remain calm. Knowing that you have planned ahead and are prepared can be very reassuring.

Students read text closely to determine what the text says.

Name ______________________________

Gather Evidence Circle clues in the text that tell you how important the writer thinks emergency supply kits are. **See annotations on previous page.**

Gather Evidence: Extend Your Ideas Do you agree with the writer? If you do, explain why. If you do not, research emergency supply kits and provide 2–3 more reasons why emergency supply kits are important.

Responses may vary.

Ask Questions Underline phrases or sentences in the text that you have questions about. **Responses may vary.**

Ask Questions: Extend Your Ideas Write two questions you would ask a disaster volunteer about preparing for an emergency.

Responses may vary.

Make Your Case How did the writer organize information in the selection? What other way do you think it could have been arranged? Explain your thinking. Draw a box around important phrases or sentences in the selection.

The writer first states the importance of having an emergency kit and then explains what should be in one. [Responses may vary as to how the selection could be rearranged.] Also see annotations on previous page.

Make Your Case: Extend Your Ideas On a separate piece of paper, write an example paragraph of another way the selection could have been arranged. Include the important phrases you drew a box around.

Responses may vary.

Students read text closely to determine what the text says.

Name ______________________________

Sort Evidence from Notes On a separate sheet of paper, complete a Three-Column Chart graphic organizer to sort information from *Living Through a Natural Disaster* into categories. You can use this graphic organizer to compare two of the disasters, using the third column for categories. You can also compare three disasters using one or two categories or compare details under three subtopics for a single category.

Responses will vary but should include a completed Three-Column Chart graphic organizer that compares natural disasters from *Living Through a Natural Disaster* in a logical way.

Form Irregular Past-Tense Verbs

DIRECTIONS Read each sentence. Then rewrite the sentence using the past-tense form of the underlined verb.

1. Hurricanes <u>bring</u> floods to Honduras and Nicaragua.

   Hurricanes brought floods to Honduras and Nicaragua.

2. The people <u>know</u> that El Niño <u>is</u> strong.

   The people knew that El Niño was strong.

3. Many areas <u>are</u> affected by El Niño.

   Many areas were affected by El Niño.

Students write routinely for a range of tasks, purposes, and audiences. Students practice various conventions of standard English.

Name ______________________

Benchmark Vocabulary

DIRECTIONS Write a sentence using each word.

organizations traumatized monitor invaluable

Responses should show contextual understanding of the word.

Write in Response to Reading

Read page 29 of *Living Through a Natural Disaster.* Is it important for people to learn from past natural disasters? Use evidence from the text in your answer.

Responses should use evidence from the text, including that "Because the consequences of natural disasters can be so terrible, it is important to learn how to handle them." Some consequences include "death, famine, disease, and homelessness."

Students demonstrate contextual understanding of Benchmark Vocabulary. Students read text closely and use text evidence in their written answers.

Name ____

Plan and Prewrite an Informational Essay Write an outline of an informational essay that will explain how climate has impacted your daily life in some way.

Responses will vary but should include an outline of an informational essay the student will write about how climate has impacted his or her daily life in some way.

Form Simple Verb Tenses

DIRECTIONS Read each sentence. Then rewrite the sentence using the form of the underlined verb that is shown in parentheses.

1. Meteorologists study data about Earth's atmosphere. (past tense)

   Meteorologists studied data about Earth's atmosphere.

2. Natural disasters affect huge groups of people. (future tense)

   Natural disasters will affect huge groups of people.

3. Disaster-relief agencies helped many people. (present tense)

   Disaster-relief agencies help many people.

Students write routinely for a range of tasks, purposes, and audiences. Students practice various conventions of standard English.

Benchmark Vocabulary

Name ______________________________

DIRECTIONS Write a sentence using each word.

damage preparations evacuate

Responses should show contextual understanding of the word.

Write in Response to Reading

Read page 5 of *Living Through a Natural Disaster,* and write a paragraph giving the name and a brief description of each type of disaster outlined in the text. Support your writing with evidence from the text.

Responses should use evidence from the text, including that tropical cyclones are "storms that develop and build over the oceans." Cyclones can cause a lot of damage if they hit coastlines. Extreme rainfall causes "water levels to rise and spill over riverbanks, flooding farmland and homes." Drought happens when rain doesn't fall for months or years. Because the plants and animals can die in drought years, "many people face economic hardship and starvation."

Students demonstrate contextual understanding of Benchmark Vocabulary. Students read text closely and use text evidence in their written answers.

Name ______________________________

Scientific Ideas

DIRECTIONS Using evidence from the text, answer the following questions about *Living Through a Natural Disaster.*

1. Why was Cyclone Tracy so destructive?

The cyclone hit Darwin, Australia, with heavy rains and winds of more than 125 miles per hour. The wind flattened buildings and blew apart the town, and the rain ruined everything inside the buildings.

2. How does human activity cause floods?

When people cut down trees, they remove the vegetation that absorbs rain. When they build houses and roads, they cover the soil that also absorbs rain. When it rains, the soil and the plants cannot absorb the water, and storm sewers might overflow.

3. What makes the plains near the Huang He in China so fertile?

The flooding of the Huang He leaves behind a layer of silt on the plains, which makes the soil fertile.

4. What caused the Huang He flood of 1933?

Heavy rains caused the river to rise above the top of the dikes. People tried to make the walls of the dikes higher, but they were unsuccessful. The river finally broke the dikes and flooded the surrounding plains.

Students analyze and respond to literary and informational text.

Name ______________________________

Writing

Draft an Informational Essay On a separate sheet of paper, write a draft of an informational essay that will explain how climate has impacted your daily life in some way.

Responses will vary but should include a draft of an informational essay about how climate has impacted the student's daily life in some way.

Conventions

Form and Use Simple Verb Tenses

DIRECTIONS Complete each sentence with the present, past, or future tense of the verb in parentheses. The verb must make sense in the sentence.

1. Extreme rainfall can **cause** many problems for people who live near rivers. (cause)
2. Hurry, the eye of the cyclone **will pass** soon! (pass)
3. Last year's drought **dried** the land. (dry)

Students write routinely for a range of tasks, purposes, and audiences. Students practice various conventions of standard English.

Name ____________________

Vowel Patterns *a, au, aw, al, augh, ough*

DIRECTIONS Choose the word with the vowel sound in **ball.** Write the word on the line.

cause **1.** The (cause/meaning) of our move was to be near family.

small **2.** Now we live in a (tiny/small) apartment.

lawn **3.** I really miss having a (lawn/yard) to run around on.

talk **4.** Sometimes we (speak/talk) about our old home.

palm **5.** The ocean and the (palm/oak) trees were wonderful.

caught **6.** We often (found/caught) fish and ate them for dinner.

always **7.** We (usually/always) agree that we are glad we moved.

thought **8.** That is because we (wanted/thought) of our family.

DIRECTIONS Write ***a, au, aw, al, augh,*** or ***ough*** to complete each word. Write the whole word on the line.

shawl **9.** I picture my grandmother wrapped in her purple sh___l.

sauce **10.** I remember the scent of her delicious tomato s___ce.

sausage **11.** I miss the s___sage she cooked for our dinner.

cough **12.** Sometimes it was so spicy, it made me c___!

taught **13.** But grandmother t___t us to enjoy what we have now.

walk **14.** We can w___k to our cousins' houses whenever we want.

call **15.** We can also c_ll grandmother to tell her we miss her.

Students apply grade-level phonics and word analysis skills.

Name ______________________________

Benchmark Vocabulary

DIRECTIONS Write a sentence using each word.

condensed resistance evaporates affects diverse habitats

Responses should show contextual understanding of the word.

Write in Response to Reading

Revisit the photographs in *Weather* and *Living Through a Natural Disaster.* In your opinion, are the captions that describe the events happening in the photographs necessary? Use specific examples from the texts to support your answer.

Responses should use evidence from the text, including that many of the captions in *Living Through a Natural Disaster* give extra information that you don't get in the text, such as the caption on page 12 (which shows modern-day Darwin). There aren't captions in *Weather*; the photographs are explained in the text.

Students demonstrate contextual understanding of Benchmark Vocabulary. Students read text closely and use text evidence in their written answers.

Name ______________________________

Contribution of Maps, Photographs, and Illustrations

DIRECTIONS Using evidence from the texts, answer the following questions about *Weather* and *Living Through a Natural Disaster.*

1. What does the diagram on page 8 of *Weather* show? How does it support the information on page 9?

   It shows the atmosphere in motion. The changing color of the diagram illustrates how the temperature of the atmosphere changes as it moves.

2. What does the diagram on page 8 of *Living Through a Natural Disaster* show? How does it support the information on page 8?

   It shows a cyclone's wall, its eye, and how the winds spiral around the eye. This helps readers understand the movement of wind and rain in a cyclone.

3. Think about these two diagrams and other diagrams in both texts. How are the authors' use of diagrams in *Weather* and *Living Through a Natural Disaster* similar?

   They both use diagrams to show the movements that create weather events or conditions.

4. How are the authors' use of maps in *Weather* and *Living Through a Natural Disaster* similar?

   They both use maps to show *where* certain weather events occur in diagrams.

5. How are the authors' use of maps in *Weather* and *Living Through a Natural Disaster* different?

   Only *Living Through a Natural Disaster* uses maps to show where a particular weather event happened.

Students analyze and respond to literary and informational text.

Name ______________________

Writing

Revise an Informational Essay On a separate sheet of paper, revise the draft of your informational essay that explains how climate has impacted your daily life.

Responses will vary but should include a revised draft of an informational essay that explains how climate has impacted the student's daily life.

Conventions

Form Simple Sentences

DIRECTIONS Use information from *Weather* and *Living Through a Natural Disaster* and the directions below to write simple sentences.

1. Write a simple sentence with a singular subject and a verb that is in the present tense.

   The atmosphere lets sunlight pass through.

2. Write a simple sentence with a plural subject and a verb that is in the past tense.

   Crops withered in the Central American drought.

3. Write a simple sentence with a singular subject and a verb that is in the past tense.

   They provided emergency aid to disaster victims.

Students write routinely for a range of tasks, purposes, and audiences. Students practice various conventions of standard English.

Benchmark Vocabulary

Name ______________________________

DIRECTIONS Write a sentence using each word.

orbits nourishes erosion irrigation

Responses should show contextual understanding of the word.

Write in Response to Reading

Explain how the authors of *On the Same Day in March* and *Living Through a Natural Disaster* use key details to support a main idea. Use specific examples from the texts to support your answer.

Responses should use evidence from the text, including that in *On the Same Day in March,* the author's key details are that the weather is different on the same day in different places. The main idea is that different places on Earth have different seasons. In *Living Through a Natural Disaster,* the author gives key details about many different disasters around the world, with the main idea that there are ways people can survive natural disasters.

Students demonstrate contextual understanding of Benchmark Vocabulary. Students read text closely and use text evidence in their written answers.

Name ______________________________

Edit a Piece of Writing On a separate sheet of paper, edit your paragraphs that explain how climate has impacted your daily life in some way. Examine your essay with a focus on word choice and sentence structure. Have you chosen the best words to say what you mean? Have you used varied sentence structure to give your writing a better flow? Keep these questions in mind as you edit your work.

Responses will vary but should include an edited version of the student's essay that features precise word choice and uses varied sentence structure.

Form Compound Sentences

DIRECTIONS Choose the conjunction *and, but, yet, or,* or *so* to correctly complete the following compound sentences about *On the Same Day in March* and *Living Through a Natural Disaster.*

1. I thought spring would never come, __**but**__ finally the March chinook is here!
2. In central Thailand in March, it is too hot to plant rice, __**and**__ it is too hot to pick rice.
3. Floods from the Huang He used to be a big problem, __**yet or but**__ today parts of the river are nearly dry.

Students write routinely for a range of tasks, purposes, and audiences. Students practice various conventions of standard English.

Benchmark Vocabulary

Name ______________________

DIRECTIONS Write a sentence using each word.

altitude continuous advances axis traumatized monitor invaluable

Responses should show contextual understanding of the word.

Write in Response to Reading

Locate related events, concepts, or processes in *On the Same Day in March, Weather,* and *Living Through a Natural Disaster.* In your opinion, which author does the best job of expressing the relationships between those events, concepts, or processes? Use specific examples from the texts to support your answer.

Responses should use evidence from the text.

Students demonstrate contextual understanding of Benchmark Vocabulary. Students read text closely and use text evidence in their written answers.

Writing

Name ________________________________

Publish and Present Think of unusual ideas for presenting your work. For example, after you have published your essay, work with the whole class or in a smaller group to coordinate the presentation of your work. Have the assigned timekeeper, recorder, and manager work together to make sure everyone participates and stays on task. Write your ideas for presenting your work on the lines below. Finally, present your essay.

Responses will vary but should include ideas for presenting the student's essay.

Conventions

Form Complex Sentences

DIRECTIONS Create a complex sentence using each pair of sentences.

1. The drought in Central America worsened. Costa Rica still did not ask for aid. **After the drought in Central America worsened, Costa Rica still did not ask for aid.**

2. The Kenyan people hurried to play in the river. It would soon dry up. **The Kenyan people hurried to play in the river because it would soon dry up.**

3. Trees absorb most of the sun's energy that falls on them. A fresh snowfall reflects most of the sun's energy. **Trees absorb most of the sun's energy that falls on them, while a fresh snowfall reflects most of the sun's energy.**

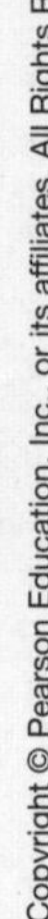

Students write routinely for a range of tasks, purposes, and audiences. Students practice various conventions of standard English.

Name ______________________________

Vowel Patterns *ei, eigh*

DIRECTIONS Read each sentence. Underline the word that has ***ei*** or ***eigh***. Write ***long a, long e,*** or ***long i*** on the line to tell what sound the vowel pattern stands for.

long a **1.** We enjoy shopping at our neighborhood bakery.

long e **2.** We always go on either Friday or Saturday.

long e **3.** Shelves of baked goods reach from floor to ceiling.

long i **4.** I'm not the right height to reach the top shelf.

long a **5.** That shelf must be eight feet high!

long a **6.** We weigh all our choices and make up our minds.

long e **7.** At last, we receive our package from the baker.

DIRECTIONS Choose a word from the Word Bank to match each clue. Write the word on the line. You will use each word just once.

Word Bank

deceive	freight	height	leisure
neighbor	rein	seize	vein

rein **8.** a strap used to control a horse

seize **9.** to grab an object

leisure **10.** free time

neighbor **11.** a person who lives nearby

height **12.** the distance up from the ground

freight **13.** cargo a truck carries from one place to another

deceive **14.** not tell the truth

vein **15.** a blood vessel in a living creature's body

Students apply grade-level phonics and word analysis skills.

Benchmark Vocabulary

Name ______________________________

DIRECTIONS Write a sentence using each word.

scratchy fierce belong pale punchy

Responses should show contextual understanding of the word.

Write in Response to Reading

Write a paragraph about the boy in the story. Describe what he is like, what he does, and how he feels. Remember to use text evidence to support your ideas.

Responses should use evidence from the text, including that he is a young boy, his mother has been working all day and is tired, he likes to play with his marble and needs to be told twice to put it away, he gets "shaky" when Mrs. Parks won't move to the back of the bus, but he also feels "strong" after she is arrested.

Students demonstrate contextual understanding of Benchmark Vocabulary. Students read text closely and use text evidence in their written answers.

Name ______________________

Writing

Write About Genre: Historical Fiction Write a paragraph in which you explain what is fiction and what is fact in the historical fiction *Back of the Bus*. Support your opinion with reasons and evidence from the text.

Responses will vary but should include an explanation of what is fiction and what is fact in *Back of the Bus*. Responses should also include reasons and evidence from the text.

Conventions

Identify Nouns

DIRECTIONS Read these sentences from *Back of the Bus*. Underline the nouns. Then circle the noun that serves as a subject in the sentence. Tell whether each noun names a person, place, animal, or thing.

1. Mama shakes "no" at me, and I hold it snug in my hand.

   Mama names a person, and *hand* names a thing.

2. That breeze is long gone, and I want me a drink real bad.

   Breeze and *drink* name things.

3. That policeman clicks them metal things on her hands, quick and loud like the screen door slammin', and off the bus they go.

   Policeman names a person, and *things, hands, door,* and *bus* name things.

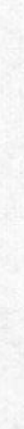

Students write routinely for a range of tasks, purposes, and audiences. Students practice various conventions of standard English.

Name ______________________________

Benchmark Vocabulary

DIRECTIONS Write a sentence using each word.

scratchy fierce belong pale punchy

Responses should show contextual understanding of the word.

Write in Response to Reading

Read *Back of the Bus*. Write a paragraph in which you state an opinion about whether Mama and the other passengers should have defended Rosa. Support your opinion with text evidence.

Responses should use evidence from the text.

Students demonstrate contextual understanding of Benchmark Vocabulary. Students read text closely and use text evidence in their written answers.

Writing

Name ______________________

Write About Theme Write a paragraph that tells the central message of *Back of the Bus*. Use examples from the text to support your choice.

Responses will vary but should include a paragraph that tells the central message of *Back of the Bus* and uses examples from the text to support it.

Conventions

Form Regular Plural Nouns

DIRECTIONS Read page 66 of *Back of the Bus*. Choose three singular nouns from the page. Add endings to them to make them plural, and write the plural noun on the line. Then write a sentence with the plural noun.

1. **winters / The winters in Alabama are very mild.**

2. **windows / The windows on the bus are hard to open.**

3. **buses / The school buses are lined up to drop the children off at the school.**

Students write routinely for a range of tasks, purposes, and audiences. Students practice various conventions of standard English.

Name ______________________________

Benchmark Vocabulary

DIRECTIONS Write a sentence using each word.

aisle jammed growly hush

Responses should show contextual understanding of the word.

Write in Response to Reading

Read *Back of the Bus*. Write a paragraph in which you state an opinion about what Mama thinks about what Rosa Parks does. Support your opinion with text evidence.

Responses should use evidence from the text.

Students demonstrate contextual understanding of Benchmark Vocabulary. Students read text closely and use text evidence in their written answers.

Name ______________________________

Real-Life Connections Between Words and Their Use

DIRECTIONS Using evidence from the text, answer the following questions about *Back of the Bus.*

1. Find the word *fierce* on page 74. Use the word *fierce* to tell about something in your life.

   Responses should include a personal connection to the word *fierce*.

2. Now use the word *fierce* to tell about something in the world.

   Possible response: A mother animal, such as a cat, will be fierce when protecting its babies.

3. Find the word *clicks* on page 77. Use the word *clicks* to tell about something in your life that makes the same noise.

   Responses should include a personal connection to the word *clicks*.

4. Now use the word *clicks* to tell about something in the world.

   Possible response: The buckle of a seatbelt clicks into place.

5. Find the phrase "pale and punchy" on page 78. The author uses this phrase to explain that the boy feels dazed. Use the phrase "pale and punchy" to describe something in your life.

   Responses should include a personal connection to the phrase "pale and paunchy."

Students analyze and respond to literary and informational text.

Name ______________________________ Sleuth Work

Don't Give Up!

What do Sonia Sotomayor, Walt Disney, Dr. Seuss, and Thomas Edison have in common? They have become famous, successful people—but they didn't start out that way!

Sonia Sotomayor has overcome many challenges. She grew up poor and lost her father when she was young. She spoke only Spanish as a child. However, she studied hard in school and became a lawyer. Today she serves on the United States Supreme Court. She is only the third woman to do so.

Walt Disney was fired from his newspaper job and told he had a poor imagination. Today, Disney's ideas inspire theme parks and a movie company.

Theodor Geisel, also known as Dr. Seuss, wrote his first book called *And to Think That I Saw It on Mulberry Street*. After many different book companies turned it down, one company printed it. He went on to write over 40 children's books.

These people might have just given up, but they *didn't*. They kept trying and became successful.

Thomas Edison didn't give up, either. He invented many things, including a long-lasting light bulb. It took him hundreds of tries before he found the materials that worked best for this invention. He never thought of himself as a failure. He said, "I have not failed. I've just found ten thousand ways that won't work."

Every time Edison tried something that didn't work, he got one step closer to finding a way that *would* work.

So the next time you're trying to learn something new or solve a problem, don't stop trying. You may be just one step away from success!

Students read text closely to determine what the text says.

Name ______________________________

Gather Evidence Box phrases and sentences in the article that explain how the author feels about failure. **See boxed annotations on previous page.**

Gather Evidence: Extend Your Ideas Did you box "These people might have just given up, but they didn't. They kept trying and became successful"? How are the clues you boxed good signs the author feels strongly about not giving up? Write one or two sentences explaining how.

Responses may vary but could include that because they kept trying, they were successful.

Ask Questions Underline two facts about one of the people in this article. Write a question that can be answered by the facts you chose.

Responses may vary but should use text evidence.

Ask Questions: Extend Your Ideas If you could talk to one of the famous people mentioned in this article, with whom would you talk and what would you ask? Make a list of the questions you would like to ask.

Responses may vary.

Make Your Case Circle what you think is the most important reason the writer gives to support the conclusion to this selection. Explain your choice below.

See annotation on previous page. Responses may vary but may include that you shouldn't let your failures stop you from trying.

Make Your Case: Extend Your Ideas On a separate sheet of paper, write a paragraph that tells another way the conclusion to the selection could have been reached. Make sure to use the important reason you circled.

Responses may vary.

Students read text closely to determine what the text says.

Writing

Name ______________________________

Author's Purpose and Forming Opinions Pretend you are going to interview Rosa Parks about taking action and making changes. On a separate sheet of paper, write ten interview questions that you would ask Rosa Parks. Then write one sentence stating an opinion about Rosa Parks's impact on the United States.

Responses will vary but should include ten interview questions for Rosa Parks about taking action and making changes and one sentence that states the student's opinion about Rosa Parks's impact on the United States.

Conventions

Form Irregular Plural Nouns

DIRECTIONS Complete each sentence below with the plural form of the noun in parentheses.

1. I watched my older brother build **shelves** (shelf) for his room.
2. There were five **men** (man) in the car.
3. Sarah watched the **geese** (goose) swim across the pond.

Students write routinely for a range of tasks, purposes, and audiences. Students practice various conventions of standard English.

Benchmark Vocabulary

Name ______________________________

DIRECTIONS Write a sentence using each word.

bravery dignity

Responses should show contextual understanding of the word.

Write in Response to Reading

Read *Back of the Bus* and *Rosa Parks: Hero of Our Time*. Using information from both texts, write a paragraph in which you explain what Rosa Parks did and how it changed things for all Americans.

Responses should use evidence from the text. Both texts tell about how Rosa Parks refused to give up her seat to a white man and that she was arrested for that. "Rosa Park: Hero of Our Time" also tells what happens later, including that she stood trial and Montgomery citizens began a bus boycott. The case went to the Supreme Court, and they declared that no African American should be forced to give up his/her seat. *Back of the Bus* also shows that Mrs. Park's action made African Americans proud.

Students demonstrate contextual understanding of Benchmark Vocabulary. Students read text closely and use text evidence in their written answers.

Name ___________________________________

Compare and Contrast

DIRECTIONS Using evidence from the texts, answer the following questions about *Rosa Parks: Hero of Our Time* and *Back of the Bus*.

1. How do both *Back of the Bus* and *Rosa Parks: Hero of Our Time* show the effect Rosa Parks's actions have on other African Americans?

   In *Back of the Bus,* the narrator describes his mother's response and says, "I see somethin' too—she's got Mrs. Parks's lightnin'-storm eyes now." This shows that her actions stirred up strong feelings in others. In *Rosa Parks: Hero of Our Time*, the author explains that African Americans "became very angry" about her arrest and "decided they would not ride the bus" the day of her trial and for a year afterward.

2. At the end of *Rosa Parks: Hero of Our Time*, the author writes, "Rosa Parks's bravery helped make life better for all Americans." How is this idea shown in *Back of the Bus?*

   Responses may vary but could include that the narrator takes his marble out, holds it up, and says, "That thing shines all brown and golden in the sunlight, like it's smilin', I think. 'Cuz it ain't gotta hide no more." This shows that her stand for justice makes the boy feel better about himself because he doesn't have to "hide" anymore.

Students analyze and respond to literary and informational text.

Name ______________________________

State an Opinion State an opinion that responds to the following prompt: *What makes a good citizen?* First, complete the following sentence frames:

1. The most important thing a good citizen does is ______________.

2. An important character trait for a good citizen to have is __________.

Then use your responses to develop your opinion statement, and write it on the lines below. Remember that you should support your opinion with reasons.

Responses will vary but should include an opinion statement about what makes a good citizen.

Use Irregular Plural Nouns

DIRECTIONS Create a sentence using the plural form of each noun.

1. child **Possible response: The children played outside all morning.**

2. deer **Possible response: Mary saw three deer running across the field.**

3. life **Possible response: That cat must have nine lives!**

Students write routinely for a range of tasks, purposes, and audiences. Students practice various conventions of standard English.

Benchmark Vocabulary

Name ______________________________

DIRECTIONS Write a sentence using each word.

immigrants hire filthy fined fired inspected

Responses should show contextual understanding of the word.

Write in Response to Reading

Read pages 8–11 from *Brave Girl*. Write a paragraph describing Clara's job based on information in the text and the illustrations.

Responses should use evidence from the text, including that Clara is a garment worker and sews women's clothing. She brings her sewing machine to work and stitches "collars, sleeves, and cuffs." Three hundred young women sit in a dark and stuffy room, which is locked.

Students demonstrate contextual understanding of Benchmark Vocabulary. Students read text closely and use text evidence in their written answers.

Name ____________________

Writing

Introduce the Topic Write a few sentences that introduce the topic for your opinion piece about what makes a good citizen. Think about your opinion statement from Lesson 4 as you write your introduction.

Responses will vary but should include several sentences that introduce the topic for an opinion piece about what makes a good citizen.

Conventions

Suffixes and Base Words

DIRECTIONS Add the suffix *-ness, -er, -less*, or *-y* to each base word from the text. Write the new word and a definition on the line.

1. dirt **Responses will vary. dirty: having dirt**

2. tall **Responses will vary. tallness: state of being tall**

3. move **mover: a person who moves things**

4. job **Responses will vary. jobless: without a job**

Students write routinely for a range of tasks, purposes, and audiences. Students practice various conventions of standard English.

Name ______________________________

Suffixes -y, -ish, -hood, -ment

DIRECTIONS Combine the base word and the suffix. Write the new word on the line.

1. pay + -ment = payment
2. cloud + -y = cloudy
3. self + -ish = selfish
4. child + -hood = childhood
5. storm + -y = stormy
6. excite + -ment = excitement
7. false + -hood = falsehood
8. baby + -ish = babyish

DIRECTIONS Add ***-y, -ish, -hood,*** or ***-ment*** to the base word in parentheses to best complete each sentence. Write the new word on the line.

childhood **9.** During my (child), we moved often.

neighborhood **10.** We live in one (neighbor) with woods and a pond.

entertainment **11.** Playing outdoors provided lots of (entertain).

snowy **12.** One (snow) day, we decided to go skating on the pond.

movement **13.** A (move) at the edge of the pond frightened us.

foolish **14.** How (fool) we felt when we saw it was our neighbor.

frosty **15.** Soon we were all skating in the (frost) air.

Students apply grade-level phonics and word analysis skills.

Name ______________________________

Benchmark Vocabulary

DIRECTIONS Write a sentence using each word.

imagined union punished pickets arrest

Responses should show contextual understanding of the word.

Write in Response to Reading

Read pages 15–17 from *Brave Girl*. Write a paragraph telling why Clara wants the factory girls to strike and what she hopes they will gain from a strike.

Responses should use evidence from the text, including that Clara wants them to strike because they are overworked, underpaid, and punished for speaking up. She hopes they get paid better and have better working conditions.

Students demonstrate contextual understanding of Benchmark Vocabulary. Students read text closely and use text evidence in their written answers.

Writing

Name ________________________________

Provide Reasons to Support an Opinion Write sentences stating three reasons that support your opinion about what makes a good citizen.

Responses will vary but should include reasons that support an opinion about what makes a good citizen.

Conventions

Prefixes and Base Words

DIRECTIONS Add the prefix *dis-, un-, over-,* or *under-* to the base words. Write the new word and a definition on the line.

1. afraid unafraid: not afraid

2. do Responses may vary. overdo: do too much

3. fed Responses may vary. underfed: not fed enough

4. pay Responses may vary. overpay: pay too much

Students write routinely for a range of tasks, purposes, and audiences. Students practice various conventions of standard English.

Benchmark Vocabulary

Name ______________________________

DIRECTIONS Write a sentence using each word.

speech meeting proposes patience revolt bravest

Responses should show contextual understanding of the word.

Write in Response to Reading

Read pages 21–23 from *Brave Girl*. What do you think about Clara's actions at the union meeting? Write a paragraph that states your opinion and supports it with reasons and evidence from the text.

Responses should use evidence from the text.

Students demonstrate contextual understanding of Benchmark Vocabulary. Students read text closely and use text evidence in their written answers.

Name ___________________________

Point of View

DIRECTIONS Using evidence from the text, answer the following questions about page 28 from *Brave Girl.*

1. Read page 28. What is the author's point of view about bringing about change in America?

   The author believes that anyone can bring about change in America.

2. What details from the text reveal the author's point of view?

   Responses may vary but could include that the author says that Clara's actions prove "that in America, wrongs can be righted." This shows that the author believes important change can happen in America. The author also says that "warriors can wear skirts and blouses" and that "the bravest hearts may beat in girls only five feet tall." This shows that the author believes anyone can bring about that change.

3. What is your point of view about bringing about change in America?

   Responses will vary.

Students analyze and respond to literary and informational text.

Name ______________________________

Writing

Create an Organizational Structure On a separate sheet of paper, write several paragraphs that answer the following prompt: *What makes a good citizen?* After writing the introduction you created in Lesson 5, organize your reasons from Lesson 6, and write one paragraph for each reason.

Responses will vary but should include several organized paragraphs that give an opinion on what makes a good citizen and then provide supporting reasons.

Conventions

Define Abstract Nouns

DIRECTIONS Underline the abstract noun(s) in each sentence from *Brave Girl.*

1. Throngs of workers pack the seats, the aisles, the walls—the hall thrums with excitement.
2. Her singing lifts the spirits of the pickcters.
3. They shorten the workweek and raise salaries.

Students write routinely for a range of tasks, purposes, and audiences. Students practice various conventions of standard English.

Name ______________________

Benchmark Vocabulary

DIRECTIONS Write a sentence using each word.

industry abuses affluent publicize negotiate hazardous

Responses should show contextual understanding of the word.

Write in Response to Reading

Read page 31 from *Brave Girl*. What were the effects of the 1909 strike? Use evidence from the text to support your answer.

Responses should use evidence from the text, including that many firms allowed workers to form unions, shortened the workweek, and increased workers' wages. Workers in other cities also struck for better working conditions and the right to form unions. "The progress made by the garment industry activists affected jobs throughout the country." Workers today "have a five-day workweek, overtime pay, and other protections."

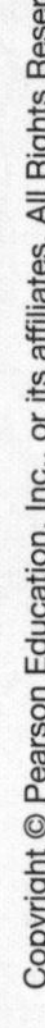

Students demonstrate contextual understanding of Benchmark Vocabulary. Students read text closely and use text evidence in their written answers.

Writing

Name ______________________________

Using Linking Words and Phrases On a separate sheet of paper, revise your paragraphs from Lesson 7 by adding linking words and phrases to link your opinion to your reasons.

Responses will vary but should include revisions to the paragraphs written in Lesson 7 to incorporate linking words and phrases that connect the student's opinion to his or her reasons.

Conventions

Abstract Nouns

DIRECTIONS Underline the abstract noun in each sentence. Then write whether the abstract noun is a subject, direct object, or an object of a preposition in the sentence.

1. Many wrongs still exist in this country. **subject**
2. Clara had a lot of courage. **object of a preposition**
3. He felt joy when he saw his new bicycle. **direct object**

Students write routinely for a range of tasks, purposes, and audiences. Students practice various conventions of standard English.

Name ______________________________

Benchmark Vocabulary

DIRECTIONS Write a sentence using each word.

immigrants arrest proposes negotiate

Responses should show contextual understanding of the word.

Write in Response to Reading

Do you think Clara Lemlich is a good subject for a biography? Why or why not? State your opinion and give reasons to support it.

Responses should use evidence from the text.

Students demonstrate contextual understanding of Benchmark Vocabulary. Students read text closely and use text evidence in their written answers.

Name ______________________________

Provide Concluding Statement and Outline Concluding Section Write a concluding statement, and outline a concluding section about how Clara Lemlich and Rosa Parks are active citizens.

Responses will vary but should include a concluding statement and an outline for a concluding section about how Clara Lemlich and Rosa Parks are active citizens.

Define Pronouns

DIRECTIONS Underline the pronoun(s) in each pair of sentences below. Then tell what noun it replaces, whether the pronoun is singular or plural, and whether it is a subject, object, or possessive pronoun.

1. Clara marched for workers' rights. She did not give up.

   Clara, singular, subject

2. The factory owners did not like Clara. She made trouble for them.

   Clara, singular, subject; owners, plural, object

3. Clara was a hero. Her bravery inspired other workers.

   Clara, singular, possessive

Students write routinely for a range of tasks, purposes, and audiences. Students practice various conventions of standard English.

Benchmark Vocabulary

Name ______________________________

DIRECTIONS Write a sentence using each word.

jammed growly hire meeting industry

Responses should show contextual understanding of the word.

Write in Response to Reading

What important point do both *Back of the Bus* and *Brave Girl* make? How does each text develop this point? Use evidence from both texts to support your answer.

Responses should use evidence from the text, including that people should stand up for their rights. *Back of the Bus* develops that idea by having a little boy tell the story of seeing Mrs. Parks refuse to give up her seat. Because of her, he feels less hidden and proud of who he is. *Brave Girl* develops that point by telling about a young woman who proves that women are strong enough to strike for their rights. Because they do, many have better working conditions today.

Students demonstrate contextual understanding of Benchmark Vocabulary. Students read text closely and use text evidence in their written answers.

Name ______________________________

Compare and Contrast

DIRECTIONS Using evidence from the texts, answer the following questions about *Back of the Bus* and *Brave Girl.*

1. How are Rosa Parks and Clara Lemlich similar?

   Responses may vary but could include that they are both people who took action to right a wrong.

2. How are the actions that Rosa Parks and Clara Lemlich took different?

   Responses may vary but could include that Rosa simply refused to obey a law that she believed was wrong, while Clara led others in taking action.

3. Which groups did Rosa Parks and Clara Lemlich help?

   Rosa Parks helped African Americans, and Clara Lemlich helped female workers.

4. What are the similarities between the groups of people Rosa Parks and Clara Lemlich helped?

   Responses may vary but could include that both African Americans and women workers were treated badly.

Students analyze and respond to literary and informational text.

Name ________________

Writing

Provide a Concluding Section Write a concluding section based on the concluding statement and outline you created in Lesson 9. First, rewrite your concluding statement from Lesson 9. Then, using the outline you created, write at least two more sentences that you can use with your concluding statement to make a concluding section.

Responses will vary but should include a concluding section based on the concluding statement and outline created in Lesson 9.

Conventions

Use Pronouns

DIRECTIONS On the lines below, write two sentences about the events in *Back of the Bus* and one sentence about the events in *Brave Girl* that include pronouns. Underline the pronouns you use in each sentence.

1. **Possible response: Rosa Parks caught his marble and rolled it back to him.**
2. **Possible response: The police officer arrested Rosa, and he took her off the bus.**
3. **Possible response: Clara hid her injuries from her parents.**

Students write routinely for a range of tasks, purposes, and audiences. Students practice various conventions of standard English.

Name ______________________________

Vowel Digraphs *oo, ew, ue, ui*

DIRECTIONS Circle each word with the vowel sound in **moon** or the vowel sound in **foot**. Then write each word in the correct column.

1. The entire school spent a day at the art center in our neighborhood.
2. It took the whole day to see all of the famous paintings and statues.
3. We looked at works by some of the art world's true masters.
4. The next day, our teacher had us make new drawings in our notebooks.
5. I drew President Lincoln wearing black wool clothing and a tall hat.

vowel sound in moon	vowel sound in foot
6. school	11. neighborhood
7. statues	12. took
8. true	13. looked
9. new	14. notebooks
10. drew	15. wool

DIRECTIONS Cross out the one word in each line that does **not** have the vowel sound in **moon** or the vowel sound in **foot**.

16. ~~build~~	soot	glue
17. hook	~~rocket~~	smooth
18. ~~button~~	bookstore	juice
19. football	stew	~~story~~
20. dew	cook	~~throat~~

Students apply grade-level phonics and word analysis skills.

Name ______________________________

Benchmark Vocabulary

DIRECTIONS Write a sentence using each word.

sly freedom resolve clambered spry absent

Responses should show contextual understanding of the word.

Write in Response to Reading

Read the final two lines of "The Little Black-Eyed Rebel" on page 123. What do you think the black-eyed rebel is trying to say? Use evidence from the text to support your answer.

Responses should use evidence from the text, including that when something important needs to be done, it may take unusual ways to accomplish it. She pretended to trade a kiss for apples to get close enough to swap the letters with the boy.

Students demonstrate contextual understanding of Benchmark Vocabulary. Students read text closely and use text evidence in their written answers.

Name ____________________

Research: Gather Information Find at least two print or digital sources to support your opinion writing. Remember that you are responding to the following prompt: *What impact did Rosa Parks have on her community?* List your sources below, and explain why each one will be helpful.

Responses will vary but should include two sources that will support the student's opinion writing and an explanation for how each source will be helpful.

Function of Pronouns

DIRECTIONS Complete each sentence with an appropriate pronoun. Then, on the line next to the sentence, write down the noun it replaces.

1. The workers were so busy that they could not fix the potholes in the road. workers
2. Kim went to the store yesterday, and she bought some apples. Kim
3. The students must practice in order to improve their writing skills. students

Students write routinely for a range of tasks, purposes, and audiences. Students practice various conventions of standard English.

Name ____________________

Benchmark Vocabulary

DIRECTIONS Write a sentence using each word.

loyal dare race justice opportunity

Responses should show contextual understanding of the word.

Write in Response to Reading

In your opinion, which author does the best job of conveying the central message of her poem? Use text evidence to support your answer.

Responses should use evidence from the text.

Students demonstrate contextual understanding of Benchmark Vocabulary. Students read text closely and use text evidence in their written answers.

Name ______________________________

Determine the Central Message

DIRECTIONS Using evidence from the texts, answer the following questions about "Brother Against Brother," "Dare," and "Where?"

1. In "Brother Against Brother," what do the soldiers see when they look "into the enemy's eyes"? How do these details point to the central message of the poem?

   Possible response: They see people they love, such as fathers, brothers, and friends. These details point to the central message that the war forced people to do the unexpected—fight against their own families.

2. What word is emphasized in "Dare"? How does this detail contribute to the central message of the poem?

   Possible response: The word *dream* is emphasized in "Dare." This emphasis contributes to the central message of being hopeful that race will not matter or stop people from doing amazing things.

3. Where are the "small places" mentioned in the poem "Where?" How does this detail add to the central message of the poem?

   Possible response: They are close to a person's home. This detail helps emphasize the central message that equality is something that matters most at "home."

Students analyze and respond to literary and informational text.

Writing

Name ______________________________

Research: Take Notes Pair up with a classmate. Take turns pretending to be Rosa Parks. Interview each other, using the ten interview questions you wrote in Lesson 3. On the lines below or on a separate sheet of paper, take notes on your partner's responses. Include direct quotations where appropriate. Then revise and rewrite your opinion from Lesson 3 about Rosa Parks's impact on the United States.

Responses will vary but should include notes on the interview with a classmate pretending to be Rosa Parks and a revised opinion statement about Rosa Parks's impact on the United States.

Conventions

Function of Pronouns in Particular Sentences

DIRECTIONS Read each pair of sentences, and underline the pronoun in the second sentence. On the line below the sentences, tell which noun the pronoun replaces and whether it serves as a subject, object, or possessive.

1. Laura Purdie Salas is an author. She wrote "Dare."
   Laura Purdie Salas; subject

2. The book includes Eleanor Roosevelt's poem "Where?" Her poem expresses an opinion about human rights.
   Eleanor Roosevelt; possessive

3. I like poems. I can read them quickly.
   poems; object

Students write routinely for a range of tasks, purposes, and audiences. Students practice various conventions of standard English.

Name ______________________________

DIRECTIONS Write a sentence using each word.

Titanic voyage cramped decks longingly

Responses should show contextual understanding of the word.

The word *amazing* is used on page 8 and page 12 of *Below Deck: A* Titanic *Story*. Why do you think the author uses this word? Think of some synonyms for the word *amazing*. If the author had used one of those synonyms instead of *amazing*, would it have changed the meaning of the sentences? Why or why not?

Responses should use evidence from the text.

Students demonstrate contextual understanding of Benchmark Vocabulary. Students read text closely and use text evidence in their written answers.

Name ____

Honoring Code Talkers

On July 26, 2001, four Native Americans received the Congressional Gold Medal. It is the highest civilian award the U.S. Congress can give. These men were survivors of the Navajo Code Talkers. The Code Talkers used their native language to send secret messages during World War II. It took about 60 years for them to be recognized for their service.

Inside the Capitol in Washington, D.C., President George W. Bush addressed the audience. He said, "Today, America honors 21 Native Americans who, in a desperate hour, gave their country a service only they could give."

Bill Toledo was a Code Talker for three years. On the island of Guam, he barely missed being hit by sniper bullets. Thanks to his quick feet, he escaped unharmed. Later, while marching through the jungle, he was mistaken for a Japanese soldier. He was taken prisoner at gunpoint. The mistake was soon realized. He was given a bodyguard so it would not happen again. The Code Talkers were very important to the war effort.

Mr. Toledo said that it's important to share his experiences with younger generations. He wants them to understand that freedom comes at a cost. He wants them to appreciate the sacrifices that service people have made. It is these sacrifices that have helped Americans keep our freedom.

Students read text closely to determine what the text says.

Name ____________________

Gather Evidence Circle phrases and sentences in the article that tell how the author feels about the Code Talkers. **Responses may vary.**

Gather Evidence: Extend Your Ideas Do you agree with the author? Explain why or why not in two or three sentences.

Responses will vary.

Ask Questions Underline two sentences in the selection that you have questions about. Using the Internet or an encyclopedia, research the questions and write the answers you find.

Responses will vary.

Ask Questions: Extend Your Ideas Write two factual questions and two opinion questions you would ask a Code Talker about his experience.

Responses may vary.

Make Your Case What do you think is most important for a reader to know about World War II to better understand this selection? How does knowing about history help you better understand selections such as this one? Draw a box around a sentence in the article that you think you would understand better if you had more historical knowledge.

Responses should use evidence from the text.

Make Your Case: Extend Your Ideas On a separate sheet of paper, work with a partner to write any historical information you can remember that would help answer your questions. Then research your questions using an encyclopedia or the Internet. **Responses will vary.**

Students read text closely to determine what the text says.

Writing

Name ______________________________

Sort Evidence into Categories Remember that you will be writing an essay that gives your opinion about Rosa Parks and how her actions helped her community. On the lines below or on a separate sheet of paper, sort into categories the evidence about Parks that you gathered from your sources in Lesson 11. After taking notes on the evidence you have gathered and sorted, determine the best way to organize the information, and create a final version of your organizer on a separate sheet of paper.

Responses will vary but should include organized evidence about Rosa Parks gathered from print and digital sources.

Conventions

Ensure Pronoun-Antecedent Agreement

DIRECTIONS Underline each pronoun and circle its antecedent. If the two agree, write *correct* on the line. If they do not agree, rewrite the sentence to correct the error in pronoun-antecedent agreement.

1. Grace put their suitcase under the bunk. **Grace put her suitcase under the bunk.**
2. The passengers danced and clapped her hands. **The passengers danced and clapped their hands.**
3. The man was tall and handsome, and his clothes looked expensive. **correct**

Students write routinely for a range of tasks, purposes, and audiences. Students practice various conventions of standard English.

Benchmark Vocabulary

Name ______________________________

DIRECTIONS Write a sentence using each word.

stationary abandon chaos panic

Responses should show contextual understanding of the word.

Write in Response to Reading

Read pages 22–40 of *Below Deck: A* Titanic *Story.* Write a paragraph that explains how the events in the second half of the story build on the events in the first half.

Responses should use evidence from the text, such as that meeting Catherine earlier in the story, and having her get Grace in trouble, led to Grace saving Catherine and Catherine's parents saving Grace by giving her a seat in the lifeboat.

Students demonstrate contextual understanding of Benchmark Vocabulary. Students read text closely and use text evidence in their written answers.

Name ______________________________

Parts of Stories

DIRECTIONS Using evidence from the text, answer the following questions about pages 22–40 from *Below Deck: A* Titanic *Story*.

1. What two events does Grace remember when she has to decide whether or not to help Catherine? How do they affect her decision?

She thinks about Catherine's accusing her earlier of knowing the boys who stole food and about her aunt's comment that she is too nice. She is uncertain at first, but she decides to help Catherine anyway because it is the right thing to do.

2. What happens after Grace gets Catherine and herself back to the main deck of the ship?

Catherine's parents see her and take her to a lifeboat, and Grace follows behind them.

3. Why is Grace allowed onto the lifeboat?

Catherine's father says that she is with them because Catherine explains to him that Grace had saved her.

4. Why do Catherine's parents say that they will take care of Grace?

Responses may vary but could include that they are grateful because she saved Catherine's life.

Students analyze and respond to literary and informational text.

Name ____________________

Plan and Prewrite an Opinion Essay Create an outline for your opinion essay about Rosa Parks.

Responses will vary but should include an outline for an opinion essay about Rosa Parks.

Form Possessives

DIRECTIONS Complete each sentence with the possessive form of the noun in parentheses.

1. Grace's (Grace) photo of Aunt Nora was in her suitcase.
2. The crewmen lowered the ship's (ship) lifeboats into the water.
3. Grace could hear the passengers' (passengers) cries of terror.

Students write routinely for a range of tasks, purposes, and audiences. Students practice various conventions of standard English.

Benchmark Vocabulary

Name ______________________

DIRECTIONS Write a sentence using each word.

future rooted launched

Responses should show contextual understanding of the word.

Write in Response to Reading

What important decisions do Grace and Catherine make toward the end of the story? How do those decisions help develop the story's central message? Support your writing with text evidence.

Responses should use evidence from the text, including that the central message (helping others is the right thing to do) is developed when Grace has to lead them both to safety even though Catherine got her in trouble earlier. Grace leads them to the top deck and to the unlaunched lifeboat. Catherine also saves Grace's life by having her parents get Grace a seat on the lifeboat.

Students demonstrate contextual understanding of Benchmark Vocabulary. Students read text closely and use text evidence in their written answers.

Name ______________________________

Draft an Opinion Essay On a separate sheet of paper, write a draft of your opinion essay about Rosa Parks and the impact of her actions on her community. Use the outline you created in Lesson 14 as a guide as you draft your essay.

Responses will vary but should include a draft of an opinion essay about Rosa Parks and the impact of her actions on her community.

Using Possessives

DIRECTIONS Rewrite each sentence to use the possessive form of the underlined noun.

1. The lights of the <u>ship</u> went out.
   The ship's lights went out.

2. The seats of the <u>lifeboat</u> were almost full.
   The lifeboat's seats were almost full.

3. The crewman would have kept Grace from entering the lifeboat if the parents of <u>Catherine</u> had not spoken up.
   The crewman would have kept Grace from entering the lifeboat if Catherine's parents had not spoken up.

Students write routinely for a range of tasks, purposes, and audiences. Students practice various conventions of standard English.

Name ______________________________

Schwa

DIRECTIONS Choose the word with a vowel that has the same sound as the underlined vowels in **about, taken, pencil, lemon,** and **circus** to complete each sentence. Write the word on the line.

afraid **1.** Kim was too (afraid/lazy) to walk the dog.

rascal **2.** If Kim opened the door, the (rascal/dog) would run off.

local **3.** Kim usually took the dog to a (nearby/local) dog park.

animals **4.** All the (animals/pets) were fetching and running.

happily **5.** Kim could let the dog run (freely/happily) there.

paper **6.** Kim kept dog treats in a (paper/plastic) bag.

hurried **7.** The dog (hurried/ran) back for a treat.

eager **8.** In fact, the dog was always (ready/eager) for a treat.

DIRECTIONS Circle the letter in each word that stands for the same sound as the underlined vowels in **about, taken, pencil, lemon,** and **circus**.

9. kitchen	**12.** family	**15.** level	**18.** ago	e, i, e(second e), a
10. river	**13.** melon	**16.** dollar	**19.** open	e, o, a, e
11. surprise	**14.** sugar	**17.** bushel	**20.** canyon	u, a, e, o

Students apply grade-level phonics and word analysis skills.

Name ______________________________

Benchmark Vocabulary

DIRECTIONS Write a sentence using each word.

imagined patience hazardous decks longingly abandon

Responses should show contextual understanding of the word.

Write in Response to Reading

Recall the main events in *Brave Girl* and *Below Deck: A* Titanic *Story*. How are Clara's and Grace's actions similar and different? Use text evidence in your response.

Responses should use evidence from the text, including that both girls' actions were similar in that both were brave and they helped others, but their actions were also different. Clara organized a group of people to strike for better working conditions, while Grace had to find a way to safety.

Students demonstrate contextual understanding of Benchmark Vocabulary. Students read text closely and use text evidence in their written answers.

Name ______________________________

Revise a Draft On a separate sheet of paper, revise the opinion essay you drafted in Lesson 15. As you revise your essay, keep in mind that your essay should address the following question: *What impact did Rosa Parks have on her community?* Add linking words and phrases to connect your ideas. Add details or make them clearer to better explain your reasons, and make sure your evidence supports your opinion.

Responses will vary but should include a revised opinion essay in which the student uses linking words and phrases to connect ideas, clear details to explain reasons, and evidence that supports his or her opinion.

Use Commas in Dialogue

DIRECTIONS Add commas to correctly punctuate the dialogue.

1. "I want to go to school," said Clara.
2. "This ship is very large," said Grace. "I suppose I must board it now."
3. Clara said, "We should go on strike!"

Students write routinely for a range of tasks, purposes, and audiences. Students practice various conventions of standard English.

Name ______________________

Benchmark Vocabulary

DIRECTIONS Write a sentence using each word.

fierce punchy bravest longingly

Responses should show contextual understanding of the word.

Write in Response to Reading

In your opinion, which author does the best job of describing characters and their roles in the events of the text? Use specific examples from the texts to support your answer.

Responses should use evidence from the text.

Students demonstrate contextual understanding of Benchmark Vocabulary. Students read text closely and use text evidence in their written answers.

Name ______________________________

Compare and Contrast

DIRECTIONS Using evidence from the texts, answer the following questions about *Brave Girl*, *Back of the Bus*, and *Below Deck*: *A* Titanic *Story*.

1. How are the actions of Rosa Parks, Clara Lemlich, and Grace similar?

Responses may vary but could include that they are all motivated by doing what they believe is right.

2. How are the effects of their actions similar?

Responses may vary but could include that their actions positively affect other people.

3. How are the consequences of Rosa Parks's and Clara Lemlich's actions similar?

Responses may vary but could include that Rosa Parks and Clara Lemlich both get into trouble for doing what they believe is right.

4. How are the consequences of Grace's and Clara Lemlich's actions different from those of Rosa Parks's actions?

Responses may vary but could include that Grace and Clara receive help in return for doing the right thing, but Rosa Parks does not receive help in the story.

Students analyze and respond to literary and informational text.

Writing

Name ______________________

Edit an Opinion Piece Read the revised version of your opinion essay closely, and correct any errors you find. Look for errors in grammar, capitalization, punctuation, and spelling. On a separate sheet of paper, write the edited version of your opinion essay.

Responses will vary but should include an edited opinion piece with correct grammar, spelling, capitalization, and punctuation.

Conventions

Use Quotation Marks in Dialogue

DIRECTIONS Add quotation marks to correctly punctuate the dialogue.

1. "I'm going to miss you, Auntie Nora," said Grace. "I love you so much."
2. Clara cried, "We must hold a general strike!"
3. "What is that policeman doing here, Mama?" I asked.

Students write routinely for a range of tasks, purposes, and audiences. Students practice various conventions of standard English.

Benchmark Vocabulary

Name ______________________________

DIRECTIONS Write a sentence using each word.

burrows release beams harbor plunked

Responses should show contextual understanding of the word.

Write in Response to Reading

How does each scene in *Rescue the Pufflings!* build on the scene before it to convey the central message of the play? Use evidence from the text to support your answer.

Responses should use evidence from the text. The first scene introduces us to the characters and what they will do in the following scenes. The second scene is when they arrive on the island and get ready, by getting boxes from the store, to rescue the pufflings. The third scene is them rescuing the puffins. And the final scene is them releasing the puffins. Each scene sets up for the next scene, when they release the pufflings. The central message is that sometimes we have to help endangered animals survive.

Students demonstrate contextual understanding of Benchmark Vocabulary. Students read text closely and use text evidence in their written answers.

Name ______________________________

Publish and Present Opinion Essays On a separate sheet of paper, write a final copy of your opinion essay that is free of errors. Then publish and present your essay by creating an audio or audio and video recording.

Responses will vary but should include a final, error-free copy of the opinion essay and an audio or audio and video recording of the essay.

Using Commas in Addresses

DIRECTIONS Add commas to correctly punctuate the sentence and addresses.

1. The children went with their parents to Houston, Texas, to visit their grandmother.

2. John and Jane Williams
987 Washington Avenue
Tucson, Arizona 63774

3. Laura and Keith Bridges
134 Main Street
Columbus, Ohio 43085

Students write routinely for a range of tasks, purposes, and audiences. Students practice various conventions of standard English.

Phonics

Name ______________________

Schwa

DIRECTIONS Circle the unaccented syllable or syllables in each word.

1. flavor	**4.** occur	**7.** level	vor, oc, el
2. arrange	**5.** merrily	**8.** gargle	ar, ri, ly, gle
3. version	**6.** cocoon	**9.** passenger	sion, co, sen, ger

DIRECTIONS Choose the word with a vowel that has the same sound as the underlined vowels in **about, taken, pencil, lemon,** and **circus**. Write the word on the line.

Answer			
cannon	**10.** believe	cannon	feeling
bustle	**11.** below	pancake	bustle
compare	**12.** compare	daily	remark
welcome	**13.** branched	resume	welcome
likable	**14.** swallow	likable	heavy
summarize	**15.** predict	summarize	review
mixture	**16.** mixture	oatmeal	fancy
decision	**17.** seashore	reckless	decision
award	**18.** award	airport	attic
visible	**19.** audio	visible	massive
tender	**20.** tender	orange	festive

Students apply grade-level phonics and word analysis skills.

Benchmark Vocabulary

Name ______________________________

DIRECTIONS Write a sentence using each word.

system goods export

Responses should show contextual understanding of the word.

Write in Response to Reading

Write a paragraph that explains what you think the second duty of government should be. Use evidence from the text to support your answer.

Responses should use evidence from the text.

Students demonstrate contextual understanding of Benchmark Vocabulary. Students read text closely and use text evidence in their written answers.

Name ______________________________

Main Idea and Details

DIRECTIONS Using evidence from the text, answer the following questions about pages 4–9 from *What Is a Government?*

1. What is the main idea of the section "What Do Governments Do?"

   A government is a system that helps the citizens in its country live together.

2. Why is the money system important in a government?

   It helps people buy and sell goods and services.

3. Which details support the main idea that all children have a right to an education?

   It helps children read, write, calculate, and learn about the world and the people in it.

4. Which details help explain the importance of passing laws?

   Laws keep people safe and healthy. Laws protect the environment.

5. Which details explain how a national government protects its country?

   It pays for armed services. It trains men and women to serve in the armed forces to protect the country.

Students analyze and respond to literary and informational text.

Name ______________________

Writing

Express a Point of View Read pages 4–9 of *What Is a Government*? Write one sentence that expresses your own point of view about something you read and one sentence that expresses an opposing point of view.

Responses will vary but should include one sentence that expresses the student's point of view about something he or she read on pp. 4–9 of *What Is a Government*? and one sentence that expresses an opposing point of view about that topic.

Conventions

Subject-Verb Agreement

DIRECTIONS Circle the form of the verb that agrees in number with the subject.

1. Governments (make/makes) laws.

2. A school (educate/educates) children.

3. They always (vote/votes) on election day.

Students write routinely for a range of tasks, purposes, and audiences. Students practice various conventions of standard English.

Name ______________________________

Benchmark Vocabulary

DIRECTIONS Write a sentence using each word.

expectations inspired exception influential ruthlessness

Responses should show contextual understanding of the word.

Write in Response to Reading

Read the paragraph about Sulayman I on page 14 and Elizabeth I on page 15. These rulers governed wisely but many other rulers did not. Do you think a wise ruler or a democracy is the best government? Support your ideas by using text evidence.

Responses should use evidence from the text.

Students demonstrate contextual understanding of Benchmark Vocabulary. Students read text closely and use text evidence in their written answers.

Name ______________________________

Text Features and Search Tools

DIRECTIONS Using evidence from the text, answer the following questions about pages 10–15 from *What Is a Government?*

1. How do the photographs and their captions on pages 10–11 help you understand how the development of governments changed communities?

   Responses will vary but could include that the image on the bottom of page 10 shows a map with irrigation systems, roads, and public buildings. These were organized and built because the city probably had a government.

2. Look at the photographs and illustrations on pages 14–15. Which image is different from the others? What important idea does it help emphasize?

   Only one image shows a female leader—Elizabeth I of England. The images help readers understand that in the past female leaders were rare.

3. Read the captions of the photographs and illustrations on pages 14–15. Which caption gives information not provided in the others? What is the information?

   The caption for the illustration of Sulayman I gives information on the type of ruler he was: "He had complete power, but he was a fair ruler." The captions for the other photographs and illustrations do not provide information on how the pictured leaders ruled.

Students analyze and respond to literary and informational text.

Name ______________________

Writing

Understand Genres Write a few sentences about an opinion genre you have recently read. Explain how you knew you were reading an opinion genre. Then state your opinion about the genre, including whether you liked reading it, how strong you thought the author's reasons were, and whether you agreed or disagreed with the author's opinion.

Responses will vary but should include a few sentences about a genre of opinion writing that the student has recently read. The sentences should explain how he or she knew it was a piece of opinion writing and describe his or her opinion about the piece of writing.

Conventions

Ensure Subject-Verb Agreement

DIRECTIONS Complete each sentence with the correct present-tense form of the verb in parentheses.

1. John **carries** (carry) his backpack to class.
2. The sailor **rows** (row) the boat.
3. The student **watches** (watch) the clock.

Students write routinely for a range of tasks, purposes, and audiences. Students practice various conventions of standard English.

Benchmark Vocabulary

Name ______________________________

DIRECTIONS Write a sentence using each word.

representatives consulted intervene

Responses should show contextual understanding of the word.

Write in Response to Reading

Write a paragraph to explain the author's point of view about democracies. Support your ideas by using text evidence.

Responses should use evidence from the text.

Students demonstrate contextual understanding of Benchmark Vocabulary. Students read text closely and use text evidence in their written answers.

Name ______________________________

The Election

It was time for the school elections. Each class was supposed to vote on who would represent it in the school congress. A committee was formed of third, fourth, and fifth graders. Its job was to choose the best voting process. Everyone had ideas about how the voting should be done.

Anton, a fifth grader, thought everyone should fill out a ballot. The voting station would be in the school cafeteria. At lunch, each student would write a candidate's name on a piece of paper and put it into a box. Then the votes would be counted.

Nisha, a fourth grader, thought that each class should vote for a representative. Then each grade would vote for those winners to select a representative for each grade.

Scotty, a third grader, thought that each grade should have an assembly to choose its representative. Someone would call out a candidate's name. Then students would raise their hands if they wanted that person to represent them. The person who got the most hands raised would be the winner.

The students went round and round about what they should do. Finally, they asked a teacher for her thoughts. "We're having a hard time agreeing on the voting process for the election," they said to the teacher.

"Why not vote on it?" asked Mrs. Hanson.

Students read text closely to determine what the text says.

Name ______________________________

Gather Evidence The election committee had several ideas for the voting process. Circle similarities between the voting suggestions.

See annotations on previous page.

Gather Evidence: Extend Your Ideas Write two sentences about the differences between the voting processes. Why do you think each student chose his or her method of voting?

Responses may vary but could include that Anton thought everyone should vote for the representatives privately, Nisha thought each grade should select a representative, and Scotty thought an assembly would be best.

Ask Questions When the committee asked the teacher for help, what questions might she have asked the committee to help it reach a decision? Circle the question she asked the committee in the selection, and then write two questions she might have asked.

See boxed annotation on previous page. Responses may vary.

Ask Questions: Extend Your Ideas Why do you think the teacher resolved the situation the way she did? Write two to three sentences explaining her reasoning.

Responses may vary but could include that the students couldn't agree on the voting process.

Make Your Case Circle an opinion held by one of the students. Give one reason that explains why that method of voting would work well.

Responses may vary.

Make Your Case: Extend Your Ideas Give one reason that explains why that method of voting would *not* work well.

Responses may vary.

Students read text closely to determine what the text says.

Name ________________________

Writing

Write About Reading Write one paragraph expressing an opinion about something you read on pages 16–21 in *What Is a Government?* Focus on one of the types of government described on those pages, and then express an opinion about the reading. Remember that you can write an opinion about the book's subject matter, organization, or illustrations, among other things.

Responses will vary but should include the student's opinion about something he or she read on pp. 16–21 in *What Is a Government?* The response may include an opinion about the book's subject matter, organization, or illustrations, among other things.

Conventions

Subject-Verb Agreement

DIRECTIONS In each sentence, underline the phrase or clause that comes between the subject and the verb. Then write whether the subject is singular or plural on the line, and circle the correct verb to complete the sentence.

1. The governments of many countries (is / are) democratic. **plural**
2. The U.S. president, who is elected by citizens, (serve / serves) a term of four years. **singular**
3. Most members of the Canadian parliament (belong / belongs) to political parties. **plural**

Students write routinely for a range of tasks, purposes, and audiences. Students practice various conventions of standard English.

Benchmark Vocabulary

Name ______________________________

DIRECTIONS Write a sentence using each word.

candidates opposition colonies

Responses should show contextual understanding of the word.

Write in Response to Reading

Write a paragraph to state your opinion about age requirements for voting. Support your ideas by using text evidence.

Responses should use evidence from the text.

Students demonstrate contextual understanding of Benchmark Vocabulary. Students read text closely and use text evidence in their written answers.

Name ______________________________

Literal and Nonliteral Meanings

DIRECTIONS Using evidence from the text, answer the following questions about pages 23–25 from *What Is a Government?*

1. What is the meaning of the word *running* in the phrase "running the government" on page 23? Is this a literal or a nonliteral meaning of the word?

Running **means "controlling" in this phrase. This is a nonliteral meaning of the word.**

2. If *running* has a literal meaning on page 23, what is a nonliteral meaning of the word? If *running* has a nonliteral meaning on page 23, what is a literal meaning of the word?

Responses may vary but could include that the literal meaning of *running* is "make something move quickly" or "operate."

3. What is the meaning of the word *heard* as it is used in the phrase "other interests are heard" on page 25? Is this a literal or a nonliteral meaning of the word?

Heard **means "considered" in the phrase "other interests are heard." This is a nonliteral meaning of the word.**

4. If *heard* has a literal meaning on page 25, what is a nonliteral meaning of the word? If *heard* has a nonliteral meaning on page 25, what is a literal meaning of the word?

A literal meaning of the word *heard* is "listened to with one's ears."

Students analyze and respond to literary and informational text.

Writing

Name ____________________

Introduce the Topic Begin an introduction for an opinion essay that responds to the following question: *What, in your opinion, is the most important function of government?* First, read the different functions of government described on pages 4–9 of *What Is a Government?* Next, decide which of those functions is the most important. Then, think about introductions that caught your attention, and brainstorm ways to catch your readers' attention. Finally, introduce the topic of government in an interesting way in two or three sentences.

Responses will vary but should include two to three sentences that introduce the topic of government in an interesting way.

Conventions

Ensure Subject-Verb Agreement in Past Tense

DIRECTIONS Complete each sentence with the correct past-tense form of the verb *to be*.

1. My old school **was** down the street from my house.
2. The town's hospitals **were** all built within the last ten years.
3. You **were** happy to get a chance to see the play.

Students write routinely for a range of tasks, purposes, and audiences. Students practice various conventions of standard English.

Name ________________

Benchmark Vocabulary

DIRECTIONS Write a sentence using each word.

participating issue protest occupation

Responses should show contextual understanding of the word.

Write in Response to Reading

Read pages 28–29 of *What Is a Government?* Write a paragraph describing an issue in your school and how you can make your feelings about the issue known. Use evidence from the text in your response.

Responses should use evidence from the text.

Students demonstrate contextual understanding of Benchmark Vocabulary. Students read text closely and use text evidence in their written answers.

Name ______________________________

Text Features and Search Tools

DIRECTIONS Using evidence from the text, answer the following questions about pages 28–32 from *What Is a Government?*

1. What is the definition of *democracy* in the glossary?

   A *democracy* is "a system of government in which citizens take part in the decision-making process."

2. What are the definitions of *parliament* and *president* in the glossary?

   Parliament is "an elected group of people who gather together to discuss public issues and make laws." A *president* is "the head of state and elected leader of a republic."

3. How do these three definitions make clear the similarities and differences between being a president and being a member of parliament in a democracy?

   Responses may vary but could include that presidents and members of parliaments are both elected by citizens in a democracy. They are different because one is part of a group that leads, and the other is a single leader.

4. Based on information in the index, on which pages of the text could you find information to help you better understand the similarities and differences between being a president and being a member of parliament?

   pages 16–19, 21, and 25

Students analyze and respond to literary and informational text.

Name ______________________

Writing

State an Opinion Write an opinion statement in response to the prompt from Lesson 4. First, reread the section of the text about the different functions of government on pages 4–9 of *What Is a Government?* Next, review your introduction from Lesson 4. Then, form an opinion about which function of government is most important. Finally, state your opinion, which may include a key fact or detail.

Responses will vary but should include the student's opinion about which function of government is most important, which may include a key fact or detail.

Conventions

Ensure Subject-Verb Agreement in Present Tense

DIRECTIONS Complete each sentence with the correct present-tense form of the verb *to write.*

1. I **write** a letter to my representative about the park near my house.
2. They **write** an e-mail to the mayor about city schools.
3. She **writes** a letter to the editor of the local newspaper about recycling.

Students write routinely for a range of tasks, purposes, and audiences. Students practice various conventions of standard English.

Name ______________________________

Final Syllables

DIRECTIONS Circle the correctly spelled word in each pair.

1. commosion (commotion)
2. (invasion) invation
3. generasion (generation)
4. posision (position)
5. relaxasion (relaxation)
6. (division) divition
7. vacasion (vacation)
8. explotion (explosion)

DIRECTIONS Add **-ture, -ive,** or **-ize** to complete each word below. Write the complete word on the line. There is only one correct choice for each word.

9. pas pasture
10. act active
11. rup rupture
12. mass massive
13. maxim maximize
14. real realize
15. cap capture
16. adven adventure

DIRECTIONS Choose four words from the above list and write a sentence for each word.

17. Sentences will vary.
18. Sentences will vary.
19. Sentences will vary.
20. Sentences will vary.

Students apply grade-level phonics and word analysis skills.

Name ____________________

Benchmark Vocabulary

DIRECTIONS Write a sentence using each word.

inspired influential

Responses should show contextual understanding of the word.

Write in Response to Reading

Read *What Is a Government?* Write a paragraph describing which ancient government you would have liked to live under. Use text evidence in your response.

Responses should use evidence from the text.

Students demonstrate contextual understanding of Benchmark Vocabulary. Students read text closely and use text evidence in their written answers.

Writing

Name ______________________________

Support an Opinion with Reasons Make a list of reasons that support your opinion about the most important function of government. First, review the descriptions on pages 4–9 of the text, your introduction from Lesson 4, and your opinion statement from Lesson 5. Then, list three reasons that support your opinion, and provide additional details for each reason, if available. Use the text to help you come up with reasons and details that support your opinion.

Responses will vary but should include three reasons—and supporting details—that support the student's opinion about what the most important function of government is.

Conventions

Ensure Subject-Verb Agreement in Future Tense

DIRECTIONS Use the future-tense form of each verb below in a sentence.

1. vote **Citizens will vote for a candidate.**

2. lead **The president will lead the country.**

3. control **A dictator will control the army.**

Students write routinely for a range of tasks, purposes, and audiences. Students practice various conventions of standard English.

Name ______________________________

Benchmark Vocabulary

DIRECTIONS Write a sentence using each word.

centuries merchant

Responses should show contextual understanding of the word.

Write in Response to Reading

Read page 84 from *Who Really Created Democracy?* Do you think the people of Athens had the right to be frustrated? Explain your answer using evidence from the text.

Responses may vary but should use evidence from the text, including that the people of Athens did have the right to be frustrated because most were poor and had to borrow money to buy food and pay taxes. They had no power and "no say in Athens's laws." The laws were so strict that people had to sell family members into slavery.

Students demonstrate contextual understanding of Benchmark Vocabulary. Students read text closely and use text evidence in their written answers.

Name ____________________

Word Relationships

DIRECTIONS Using evidence from the text, answer the following questions about pages 83–85 from *Who Really Created Democracy?*

1. Find the word *debts* on page 83. What are debts?

   Debts are sums of money that are owed to someone.

2. Use the word *debts* in a sentence about something in real life.

   Sample response: I don't have any debts because I don't owe anyone money.

3. On page 83, find the word *frustrated.* Why are the farmers frustrated?

   They are poor and owe money to the wealthy rulers.

4. Read page 85. Why would the colonists be frustrated?

   The colonists would be frustrated because they pay a lot of taxes, do not receive fair trials, and cannot vote for members of Parliament.

5. Use the word *frustrated* in a sentence about something in real life.

   Sample response: I'm frustrated when my mom won't even listen to my side of the story.

Students analyze and respond to literary and informational text.

Name ______________________

Writing

Create an Organizational Structure Use the following steps to create a structure for your opinion piece:

1. On a separate sheet of paper, create a Web B graphic organizer with your opinion statement from Lesson 5 in the center circle.
2. Use your list of reasons from Lesson 6 to fill in the outer circles with reasons that support your opinion statement.
3. Add bullet points with additional details about the reasons.
4. Number the reasons in the order you will use them.

Then use the graphic organizer to write the first draft of your opinion piece on a separate sheet of paper.

Responses will vary but should include a Web B graphic organizer that includes the student's opinion statement, reasons, and supporting details. It should also include a draft of the student's opinion piece.

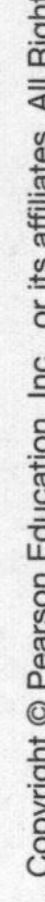

Conventions

Identify Antecedents for Pronouns

DIRECTIONS Read the sentences. On the line, write which word is the antecedent for the underlined pronoun(s). Remember that more than one pronoun can refer to the same antecedent.

1. The wealthy lawmakers know <u>they</u> can't continue to fight the masses. **lawmakers**
2. The king is furious. <u>He</u> is making harsher laws. **king**
3. In a democracy, people—rich and poor—make laws together. <u>They</u> also choose <u>their</u> own leaders. **people**

Students write routinely for a range of tasks, purposes, and audiences. Students practice various conventions of standard English.

Benchmark Vocabulary

Name ____________________

DIRECTIONS Write a sentence using each word.

aristocrat unrest trials

Responses should show contextual understanding of the word.

Write in Response to Reading

Read page 86 from *Who Really Created Democracy?* Write a paragraph about Solon's power in Athens. Support your writing by using text evidence.

Responses should use evidence from the text, including that the wealthy rulers turned the government over to Solon. He was given all the power, and he could have created any laws he wanted.

Students demonstrate contextual understanding of Benchmark Vocabulary. Students read text closely and use text evidence in their written answers.

Name ______________________________

Use Linking Words to Connect Ideas On a separate sheet of paper, rewrite your opinion essay, and use linking words and phrases to connect opinions and reasons. Refer to your Web B graphic organizer as a reminder of the organizational structure that shows how the reasons and details are related to your opinion. Then add linking words and phrases, such as *because*, *so*, *therefore*, and *as a result*, to your essay to connect your reasons to your opinions.

Responses will vary but should include a rewritten opinion essay that uses linking words and phrases to connect opinions and reasons.

Ensure Pronoun-Antecedent Agreement

DIRECTIONS Complete each sentence with a pronoun that agrees with the underlined noun or pronoun.

1. <u>Citizens</u> of Athens worried that **they** would have no power.
2. <u>Solon</u> loved **his** city and made important improvements to its government.
3. <u>Some</u> of the colonists were forced to let British soldiers stay in **their** homes.

Students write routinely for a range of tasks, purposes, and audiences. Students practice various conventions of standard English.

Name ______________________________

Benchmark Vocabulary

DIRECTIONS Write a sentence using each word.

control serve

Responses should show contextual understanding of the word.

Write in Response to Reading

Write an opinion paragraph about the ruler Hippias. How do you feel about his laws and policies? Support your writing by using text evidence.

Responses should use evidence from the text.

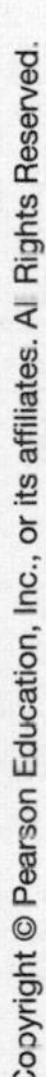

Students demonstrate contextual understanding of Benchmark Vocabulary. Students read text closely and use text evidence in their written answers.

Writing

Name ______________________________

Provide a Concluding Statement Write a concluding statement for your opinion piece. Review the ideas for a concluding statement that you wrote in your Web B graphic organizer. Then choose the best idea and write a concluding statement, which can also be a question.

Responses will vary but should include a concluding statement for the student's opinion piece.

Conventions

Produce Simple Sentences

DIRECTIONS Read page 92 of *Who Really Created Democracy?* Write three simple sentences about Peisistratus.

1. **Possible response: Peisistratus was rich and powerful.**
2. **Possible response: He built water channels.**
3. **Possible response: He died in 527 BC.**

Students write routinely for a range of tasks, purposes, and audiences. Students practice various conventions of standard English.

Name ______________________________

Benchmark Vocabulary

DIRECTIONS Write a sentence using each word.

council judicial executive legislative hurdles

Responses should show contextual understanding of the word.

Write in Response to Reading

Write an opinion paragraph about the author's point of view about who won the "race for democracy." Use text evidence to support your opinion.

Responses should use evidence from the text.

Students demonstrate contextual understanding of Benchmark Vocabulary. Students read text closely and use text evidence in their written answers.

Name ______________________________

Distinguish Points of View

DIRECTIONS Using evidence from the text, answer the following questions about pages 96–98 from *Who Really Created Democracy?*

1. What is the author's point of view about Cleisthenes? Explain your answer.

   The author thinks Cleisthenes is a good ruler. He tells about all his positive actions and says nothing negative about him.

2. What is your point of view about Cleisthenes?

   Responses may vary.

3. What is the author's point of view about the winner of the race to democracy? Explain your answer.

   The author thinks the Athenians won the race, but that in some ways it still continues. The author explains that Athenians were the first to call a type of government a democracy and that some people are still fighting for democracy.

4. What is your point of view about the winner of the race to democracy?

   Responses may vary.

Students analyze and respond to literary and informational text.

Name ______________________________

Provide a Concluding Section Write a concluding section for your opinion piece. Refer to your Web B graphic organizer for ideas to include in your concluding section. As you think about how to bring your piece to a logical, satisfying ending, consider what final idea you want the reader to take away. Then write the concluding section for your opinion piece on the lines below.

Responses will vary but should include a concluding section for an opinion piece.

Produce Compound Sentences

DIRECTIONS Combine each pair of sentences using *so, or, and,* or *but*.

1. The new government divides power. It gives people a voice.

The new government divides power, and it gives people a voice.

2. The people of Athens were the first to form a democracy. They win the "race for democracy."

The people of Athens were the first to form a democracy, so they win the "race for democracy."

Students write routinely for a range of tasks, purposes, and audiences. Students practice various conventions of standard English.

Name ______________________

Prefixes *im-*, *in-*

DIRECTIONS For each definition, write a word on the line that begins with ***im***- or ***in***-.

1. not mature immature
2. not complete incomplete
3. not sincere insincere
4. not polite impolite
5. not perfect imperfect
6. not movable immovable
7. not dependent independent
8. not capable incapable
9. not personal impersonal
10. not possible impossible
11. not correct incorrect
12. not direct indirect
13. not practical impractical
14. not probable improbable
15. not pure impure

DIRECTIONS Now write three sentences of your own. In each sentence, include at least one of the ***im-*** or ***in-*** words from above.

16. Sentences will vary.
17. Sentences will vary.
18. Sentences will vary.

Students apply grade-level phonics and word analysis skills.

Benchmark Vocabulary

Name ______________________________

DIRECTIONS Write a sentence using each word.

representatives candidate aristocrat unrest

Responses should show contextual understanding of the word.

Write in Response to Reading

Skim *Who Really Created Democracy?* and *What Is a Government?* Select one of the texts, and write a paragraph explaining its main idea. Use text evidence in your response.

Responses should use evidence from the text.

Students demonstrate contextual understanding of Benchmark Vocabulary. Students read text closely and use text evidence in their written answers.

Name ______________________

Compare and Contrast

DIRECTIONS Using evidence from the texts, answer the following questions about *What Is a Government?* and *Who Really Created Democracy?*

1. What is one similarity between the ways *What Is a Government?* and *Who Really Created Democracy?* describe democracy?

Responses may vary but could include that both texts stress that forming and maintaining a democracy takes a lot of work on the part of all its citizens.

2. What is one difference between the ways *What Is a Government?* and *Who Really Created Democracy?* describe democracy?

Responses may vary but could include that *What Is a Government?* describes the parts of democracy, while *Who Really Created Democracy?* describes the conflict that leads to the formation of a democracy.

3. What is one similarity between the ways *What Is a Government?* and *Who Really Created Democracy?* describe voting?

Responses may vary but could include that both texts emphasize the importance of voting for citizens.

4. What is one difference between the ways *What Is a Government?* and *Who Really Created Democracy?* describe voting?

Responses may vary but could include that only *What Is a Government?* describes the voting process.

Students analyze and respond to literary and informational text.

Writing

Name ______________________

Gather Information to Build Knowledge Find print and digital sources on forms of government or individual rights. On the lines below, write the title of each source, the information each source can provide, and an explanation of why each source is reliable.

Responses will vary but should include a list of print and digital sources on forms of government or individual rights. The list should include the title of each source, the information each source can provide, and an explanation of why each source is reliable.

Conventions

Define Complex Sentences

DIRECTIONS Underline the subordinate clause in each complex sentence. Circle the subordinating conjunction.

1. No laws are made in Athens unless they are approved by the Assembly.
2. The Americans actually studied Athens's ancient democracy when they designed their government.
3. After leaders debated many issues, they finally came to an agreement.

Students write routinely for a range of tasks, purposes, and audiences. Students practice various conventions of standard English.

Benchmark Vocabulary

Name ______________________________

DIRECTIONS Write a sentence using each word.

cooperating delegates anxious

Responses should show contextual understanding of the word.

Write in Response to Reading

Read pages 100–101. Write a paragraph describing the events leading up to the start of the convention.

Responses should use evidence from the text, including that "representatives from the thirteen colonies met in 1776 to write the Declaration of Independence" because they wanted to rule themselves. Colonists formed a government and fought the Revolutionary War to win freedom. After ten years, though, the government wasn't working well, and the colonies weren't cooperating. There was no President and no way to raise money. The leaders were worried and held a meeting, called a convention, to try to solve the problems.

Students demonstrate contextual understanding of Benchmark Vocabulary. Students read text closely and use text evidence in their written answers.

Name ___________________________

Main Idea and Details

DIRECTIONS Using evidence from the text, answer the following questions about pages 99–104 from *A More Perfect Union*.

1. After the revolution has ended, what problems does the United States face?

The people are poor, the states are not working together, and there is no president to lead the country.

2. What do the leaders plan?

They plan to hold a special meeting in Philadelphia.

3. What is the main idea on pages 102–103? Which details on pages 102–103 support the main idea?

Main idea: Important men already knew each other and were anxious to help their country. Supporting details: men who had served in government traveled to Philadelphia. They voted for George Washington as their leader, and James Madison took notes.

4. What is the main idea on page 104? Which details on page 104 support the main idea?

Main idea: The men made rules to help the convention run smoothly. Supporting details: Each state had one vote, a majority would rule, and the meetings were secret until after the convention.

Students analyze and respond to literary and informational text.

Name ______________________________ **Writing**

Take Brief Notes on Sources Take notes on key facts and details from pages 100–104 of *A More Perfect Union* on the lines below. Then, on a separate sheet of paper, write your notes in a T-Chart graphic organizer.

Responses will vary but should include notes on key facts and details from pp. 100–104 of *A More Perfect Union* and a T-Chart in which the student organizes his or her notes.

Conventions

Simple, Compound, and Complex Sentences

DIRECTIONS Write whether the following sentences are simple, compound, or complex. Underline coordinating conjunctions and circle subordinating conjunctions.

1. I walked to school, and I was late. **compound**
2. My stomach hurts. **simple**
3. I am going to the game after I finish my homework. **complex**

Students write routinely for a range of tasks, purposes, and audiences. Students practice various conventions of standard English.

Benchmark Vocabulary

Name ______________________________

DIRECTIONS Write a sentence using each word.

compromise document

Responses should show contextual understanding of the word.

Write in Response to Reading

Read page 109 of *A More Perfect Union.* After agreeing upon the Great Compromise, some delegates took a vacation while others continued working. Write a few sentences that explain why this happened.

Responses should use evidence from the text, including that the delegates who were not part of the Committee of Detail took a short vacation. The Committee gathered with "all the parts of the new plan for the Constitution and wrote a first draft." Then all of the delegates returned to the convention to review the draft.

Students demonstrate contextual understanding of Benchmark Vocabulary. Students read text closely and use text evidence in their written answers.

Name ______________________________

America's National Bird

In 1782, the American bald eagle became the symbol of the United States. It was chosen because it's a majestic and strong bird. How did this bird get chosen?

After the Declaration of Independence was signed in 1776, a committee was asked to research a symbol for our new country. This committee included Thomas Jefferson, John Adams, and Benjamin Franklin. They presented an illustration of a woman called "Liberty" holding a shield.

Congress wasn't impressed. It turned to a Philadelphia artist. The artist's design included a golden eagle. This species wasn't unique to the United States. After some research, Congress chose the American bald eagle. Today, the eagle is pictured on our country's seal, money, and on many stamps.

Not everyone liked this symbol. Benjamin Franklin shared his displeasure in a letter to his daughter in 1784. He said, "For my own part I wish the Bald Eagle had not been chosen the Representative of our Country. He is a Bird of bad moral Character." Franklin felt the American Bald Eagle stole food from other birds and was a coward.

However, Franklin was happy to see that the illustration of the eagle looked more like a turkey. He felt the turkey was a more appropriate symbol. Franklin believed the turkey was courageous in its own way.

Nevertheless, the American bald eagle still represents our country. President John F. Kennedy agreed with the Founding Fathers and once wrote, "The fierce beauty and proud independence of this great bird aptly symbolizes the strength and freedom of America."

Students read text closely to determine what the text says.

Sleuth Work

Name ______________________________

Gather Evidence Circle details that Benjamin Franklin used in his argument against the American bald eagle as our country's national symbol. **See annotations on previous page.**

Gather Evidence: Extend Your Ideas Write details that Benjamin Franklin used in his argument in favor of turkeys as our country's national symbol. Do you agree with his argument? Explain why in one to two sentences.

Details: He felt the turkey was more appropriate; the turkey was courageous. Opinion responses will vary.

Ask Questions You are on a committee to decide what mammal should be our country's symbol. Underline details from the article to support your decision. **See annotations on previous page.**

Ask Questions: Extend Your Ideas What questions would you research to inform your decision? Write at least two questions.

Responses will vary.

Make Your Case Underline two pieces of information from the selection that you think could have been better explained with an illustration. **Responses will vary.**

Make Your Case: Extend Your Ideas What do you think is the most interesting information you learned in this selection that is provided only by the images and not by the text? Explain.

Responses will vary.

Students read text closely to determine what the text says.

Name ______________________

Writing

Sort Evidence On a separate sheet of paper, rewrite notes from Lesson 12, sorting them into the following categories:

- People at the Convention
- Details About the Convention
- New Ideas
- Problems
- Solutions

Decide which facts and details from pages 100–104 belong in each category. Then add notes from pages 105–109 of *A More Perfect Union*.

Responses will vary but should include notes on pp. 100–109 sorted into categories.

Conventions

Capitalize Appropriate Words in Titles

DIRECTIONS Write the titles using correct capitalization.

1. connecticut compromise **Connecticut Compromise**

2. new jersey plan **New Jersey Plan**

3. declaration of independence **Declaration of Independence**

Students write routinely for a range of tasks, purposes, and audiences. Students practice various conventions of standard English.

Benchmark Vocabulary

Name ______________________________

DIRECTIONS Write a sentence using each word.

unanimous proposed

Responses should show contextual understanding of the word.

Write in Response to Reading

Explain the meaning of "the spirit of compromise" on page 110. Support your writing with text evidence.

Responses should use evidence from the text, including that not everyone agreed on every point so every sentence was "argued, debated, and discussed" until the delegates agreed. Page 108 says that compromise is when "Each side had given up something it wanted in order to create a plan that both sides could accept." The "spirit of compromise" is the willingness to work together, knowing you don't get everything you want but you will get some things.

Students demonstrate contextual understanding of Benchmark Vocabulary. Students read text closely and use text evidence in their written answers.

Name ______________________

Literal and Nonliteral Meanings

DIRECTIONS Using evidence from the text, answer the following questions about pages 110–119 from *A More Perfect Union.*

1. On page 111, the text says that some of the delegates "left the convention in anger." What does this phrase mean? Is it literal or nonliteral? Explain.

   It is nonliteral. It means that the delegates walked out of the building while having mad or angry feelings.

2. Read the following sentence from page 114: "Much hard work still lay ahead." Is this sentence literal or nonliteral? Explain your answer.

   It is a nonliteral sentence. It means that there was still a lot of work they needed to do.

3. Explain the phrase "serve his country well" on page 116.

   It means that George Washington would do his best as the leader of the United States of America.

4. What is the meaning of the following phrase from page 115: "afraid the government would be too strong"?

   It means that many people feared that the government might have too much power and cause problems for them.

Students analyze and respond to literary and informational text.

Writing

Name ________________________________

Plan and Prewrite On the lines below or on a separate sheet of paper, write an outline for an opinion piece about forms of government or individual rights as presented in this unit. Use evidence from the texts in this unit to support your opinion. Use Roman numerals and lowercase letters to organize your reasons and evidence.

Responses will vary but should include an outline for an opinion piece on forms of government or individual rights that uses evidence from the texts in this unit.

Conventions

Define Adverbs

DIRECTIONS Circle the adverb in each sentence, and underline the word that the adverb modifies. Tell what information the adverb gives.

1. The new Congress began to work immediately.
   Immediately **tells when the new Congress began to work.**

2. Parchment is a very special kind of paper.
   Very **tells how special the paper was.**

3. Others would have signed the document, but they went home early.
   Early **tells when the others went home.**

Students write routinely for a range of tasks, purposes, and audiences. Students practice various conventions of standard English.

Name ____________________

Benchmark Vocabulary

DIRECTIONS Write a sentence using each word.

cooperating compromise

Responses should show contextual understanding of the word.

Write in Response to Reading

Read pages 104–108 of *A More Perfect Union*. Write a paragraph explaining why the delegates came up with the Connecticut Compromise.

Responses should use evidence from the text, including that some delegates came up with a new government that would be elected by the people and would have three parts: a President, a congress, and a law court. The number of delegates from each state would depend on the size of the state. This was the Virginia Plan. Small states didn't like that, so they created the New Jersey Plan that kept much of the old government and said that all states would have the same number of representatives. The Connecticut Compromise included some parts of each plan, along with some new ideas.

Students demonstrate contextual understanding of Benchmark Vocabulary. Students read text closely and use text evidence in their written answers.

Name ______________________________

Historical Events

DIRECTIONS Using evidence from the text, answer the following questions about *A More Perfect Union.*

1. Why did the thirteen colonies fight the Revolutionary War?

   The thirteen colonies fought the Revolutionary War to win their independence from England.

2. Why did the members of the Committee of Detail not take a vacation?

   They wanted to work on writing a first draft of the Constitution so that the other delegates would have a document to debate when they came back from their vacations.

3. Why didn't all the delegates sign the new Constitution?

   Some of the delegates would not sign because they were not happy with the new Constitution. Others didn't sign because they had to return home early.

4. Why was the Bill of Rights added to the Constitution?

   The Bill of Rights was added to the Constitution because people were worried that certain important rights wouldn't be protected.

Students analyze and respond to literary and informational text.

Name ______________________________ Writing

Draft Using the outline you wrote in Lesson 14, write a first draft of your opinion essay on forms of government or individual rights. Be sure to use evidence from the texts to support your opinion. Write your draft on a separate sheet of paper.

Responses will vary but should include a first draft of an opinion essay on forms of government or individual rights. The draft should include text evidence that supports the student's opinion.

Conventions

Function of Adverbs

DIRECTIONS Write three sentences that include adverbs about the events described in *A More Perfect Union*. Underline the adverbs you use.

1. **Possible response: The delegates worked hard to fix the U.S. government.**
2. **Possible response: They carefully discussed the issues facing their young country.**
3. **Possible response: James Madison never missed a meeting.**

Students write routinely for a range of tasks, purposes, and audiences. Students practice various conventions of standard English.

Name ______________________________

Related Words

DIRECTIONS Choose the word that best matches each clue. Write the word on the line.

1. coverings for the body — cloth clothes — **clothes**
2. a person who plays sports — athlete athletics — **athlete**
3. a person's handwritten name — sign signature — **signature**
4. to wash — bath bathe — **bathe**
5. the world of living things — natural nature — **nature**

DIRECTIONS Read each pair of related words. Underline the parts that are spelled the same but pronounced differently. Write a sentence using one of the words in each pair.

6. feel — felt — **Sentences will vary.**
7. keep — kept — **Sentences will vary.**
8. decision — decide — **Sentences will vary.**
9. mean — meant — **Sentences will vary.**
10. definition — define — **Sentences will vary.**
11. volcanic — volcano — **Sentences will vary.**
12. pleasant — please — **Sentences will vary.**
13. relative — relate — **Sentences will vary.**
14. sign — signal — **Sentences will vary.**
15. repetition — repeat — **Sentences will vary.**

Students apply grade-level phonics and word analysis skills.

Benchmark Vocabulary

Name ____________________

DIRECTIONS Write a sentence using each word.

absolute exception delegates unanimous

Responses should show contextual understanding of the word.

Write in Response to Reading

Write a paragraph in which you compare and contrast the main ideas of *A More Perfect Union* and *What Is a Government?* Explain how key details support the main idea in each text.

Responses should use evidence from the text.

Students demonstrate contextual understanding of Benchmark Vocabulary. Students read text closely and use text evidence in their written answers.

Writing

Name ______________________

Revise Revise the draft of the opinion essay you wrote in Lesson 15. Use the following steps to revise your essay:

1. Revise your work based on the peer feedback you have received.
2. Make sure you have clearly stated your opinion.
3. Make sure you have supported your opinion with reasons.
4. Make sure you have supported each reason with evidence from the text(s).

Write your revised draft on a separate sheet of paper.

Responses will vary but should include a revision of the opinion essay drafted in Lesson 15.

Conventions

Function of Adverbs

DIRECTIONS Circle the adverb in each sentence. Then underline the word it modifies. On the line below the sentence, write whether it tells how, when, or where something happened.

1. Transportation systems help people easily move from place to place.

   It tells how the people move.

2. The bill soon became a law.

   It tells when the bill became a law.

3. Delaware approved the new Constitution, and four other states quickly followed.

   It tells how the states followed Delaware.

Students write routinely for a range of tasks, purposes, and audiences. Students practice various conventions of standard English.

Benchmark Vocabulary

Name ___________________________________

DIRECTIONS Write a sentence using each word.

aristocrat council anxious

Responses should show contextual understanding of the word.

Write in Response to Reading

Skim *A More Perfect Union* and *Who Really Created Democracy?* Write a paragraph comparing and contrasting the information they provide about the early history of the United States. Use evidence from both texts in your response.

Responses should include text evidence, including that both books tell the early beginnings of the United States. *Who Really Created Democracy* tells much more about the early struggles with King George III of England; *A More Perfect Union* only gives one page to that topic. Most of *A More Perfect Union* is about the convention and the writing of the Constitution of the United States. *Who Really Created a Democracy* doesn't tell about that, just that the system created is a democracy.

Students demonstrate contextual understanding of Benchmark Vocabulary. Students read text closely and use text evidence in their written answers.

Name ____

Compare and Contrast

DIRECTIONS Using evidence from the texts, answer the following questions about *Who Really Created Democracy?* and *A More Perfect Union*.

1. How are the texts' descriptions of the colonists' experience under British rule similar?

Responses may vary but could include that both texts describe the colonists' desire to govern themselves.

2. How are the texts' descriptions of the colonists' experience under British rule different?

Responses may vary but could include that only *Who Really Created Democracy?* describes the events that made the colonists want to govern themselves.

3. How are the texts' descriptions of the development of the American government similar?

Responses may vary but could include that both texts describe the debating and compromise that were involved in establishing the country's government.

4. How are the texts' descriptions of the development of the American government different?

Responses may vary but could include that only *Who Really Created Democracy?* explains that the leaders who developed it studied past governments.

Students analyze and respond to literary and informational text.

Name ______________________________

Writing

Editing Edit the revised draft of your opinion essay from Lesson 16. Correct spelling, capitalization, and punctuation errors. Then make sure that you have varied your sentence structure. Finally, write an edited version of your essay on a separate sheet of paper.

Responses will vary but should include an edited draft of the student's revised opinion essay.

Conventions

Comparative and Superlative Adverbs

DIRECTIONS Complete the following sentences with the comparative or superlative form of the adverb in parentheses.

1. Modern governments include women **more often** (often) than past governments.
2. Which Athenian worked **hardest** (hard) to bring democracy to Athens—Cleisthenes, Solon, or Peisistratus?
3. Some delegates arrived **later** (late) to Philadelphia than others.

Students write routinely for a range of tasks, purposes, and audiences. Students practice various conventions of standard English.

Benchmark Vocabulary

Name ______________________________

DIRECTIONS Write a sentence using each word.

expectations consulted legislative judicial executive document

Responses should show contextual understanding of the word.

Write in Response to Reading

Skim *What Is a Government?*, *Who Really Created Democracy?*, and *A More Perfect Union*. In your opinion, which author's point of view best reflects your own? Use specific examples from the texts to support your answer.

Responses should use evidence from the text.

Students demonstrate contextual understanding of Benchmark Vocabulary. Students read text closely and use text evidence in their written answers.

Name ______________________________

Publish and Present Determine how you would like to publish and present your opinion essay. Then write your plans for a presentation on the lines below.

Responses will vary but should include plans for presenting the student's opinion essay.

Comparative and Superlative Adverbs

DIRECTIONS On the lines below, write two sentences that use comparative adverbs and one sentence that uses a superlative adverb.

1. **Some delegates left the convention more happily than others.**
2. **Technology helps people vote more easily.**
3. **People who go to war for their freedom fight the hardest.**

Students write routinely for a range of tasks, purposes, and audiences. Students practice various conventions of standard English.